everyday Phonics

Intervention Activities

Table of Contents

Using Everyday Phonics Intervention Activities

Current research identifies phonemic awareness and phonics as the essential skills for reading success.

- **Phonemic awareness** is the ability to notice, think about, and work with the individual sounds in spoken words. Before children learn to read print, they need to become aware of how the sounds in words work. They must understand that words are made up of speech sounds, or phonemes.

- **Phonics** instruction teaches children the relationships between the letters (graphemes) of written language and the individual sounds (phonemes) of spoken language. Children learn to use the relationships to read and write words. Knowing the relationships will help children recognize familiar words accurately and automatically, and "decode" new words.

Although some students master these skills easily during regular classroom instruction, many others need additional re-teaching opportunities to master these essential skills. The Everyday Phonics Intervention Activities series provides easy-to-use, five-day intervention units for Grades K–5. These units are structured around a research-based Model-Guide-Practice-Apply approach. You can use these activities in a variety of intervention models, including Response to Intervention (RTI).

Getting Started

In just five simple steps, Everyday Phonics Intervention Activities provides everything you need to identify students' phonetic needs and to provide targeted intervention.

1. PRE-ASSESS to identify students' Phonemic Awareness and Phonics needs.

Use the pre-assessment to identify the skills your students need to master.

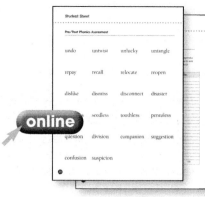

2. MODEL the skill.

Every five-day unit targets a specific phonetic element. On Day 1, use the teacher prompts and reproducible activity page to introduce and model the skill.

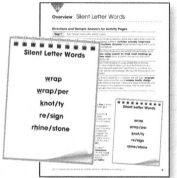

Day 1

3. GUIDE PRACTICE and APPLY.

Use the reproducible practice activities for Days 2, 3, and 4 to build students' understanding and skill-proficiency.

Day 2 **Day 3** **Day 4**

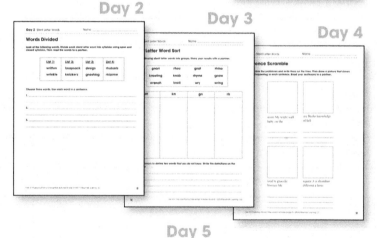

Day 5

4. MONITOR progress.

Administer the Day 5 reproducible assessment to monitor each student's progress and to make instructional decisions.

5. POST-ASSESS to document student progress.

Use the post-assessment to measure students' progress as a result of your interventions.

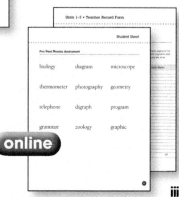

Standards-Based Phonemic Awareness
& Phonics Skills in Everyday Intervention Activities

The Phonemic Awareness and Phonics skills found in the Everyday Intervention Activities series are introduced developmentally and spiral from one grade to the next. The chart below shows the skill areas addressed at each grade level in this series.

Everyday Phonics Intervention Activities Series Skills	K	1	2	3	4	5
Phonemic Awareness	✔	✔	✔	✔		
Letter Identification and Formation	✔	✔				
Sound/Symbol Relationships	✔	✔				
Short Vowels		✔				
Consonants		✔				
Long Vowels			✔	✔		
Blends			✔	✔		
Digraphs			✔	✔		
Variant Vowels			✔	✔		
CVCe Syllable Patterns			✔	✔	✔	✔
Closed Syllable Patterns				✔	✔	✔
Open Syllable Patterns				✔	✔	✔
r-Controlled Syllable Patterns				✔	✔	✔
Diphthongs				✔	✔	✔
Silent Letters				✔	✔	✔
Regular and Irregular Plurals				✔	✔	✔
Contractions					✔	✔
Prefixes					✔	✔
Compound Words					✔	✔
Comparatives						✔
Greek and Latin Roots						✔
Homographs and Homophones						✔
Word Origins						✔

Using Everyday Intervention for RTI

According to the National Center on Response to Intervention, RTI "integrates assessment and intervention within a multi-level prevention system to maximize student achievement and to reduce behavior problems." This model of instruction and assessment allows schools to identify at-risk students, monitor their progress, provide research-proven interventions, and "adjust the intensity and nature of those interventions depending on a student's responsiveness."

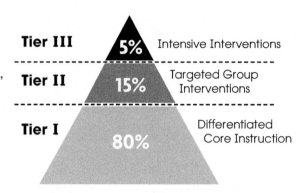

RTI models vary from district to district, but the most prevalent model is a three-tiered approach to instruction and assessment.

The Three Tiers of RTI	Using Everyday Intervention Activities
Tier I: Differentiated Core Instruction • Designed for all students • Preventive, proactive, standards-aligned instruction • Whole- and small-group differentiated instruction • Ninety-minute, daily core reading instruction in the five essential skill areas: phonics, phonemic awareness, comprehension, vocabulary, fluency	• Use whole-group comprehension mini-lessons to introduce and guide practice with comprehension strategies that all students need to learn. • Use any or all of the units in the order that supports your core instructional program.
Tier II: Targeted Group Interventions • For at-risk students • Provide thirty minutes of daily instruction beyond the ninety-minute Tier I core reading instruction • Instruction is conducted in small groups of three to five students with similar needs	• Select units based on your students' areas of need (the pre-assessment can help you identify these). • Use the units as week-long, small-group mini-lessons.
Tier III: Intensive Interventions • For high-risk students experiencing considerable difficulty in reading • Provide up to sixty minutes of additional intensive intervention each day in addition to the ninety-minute Tier I core reading instruction • More intense and explicit instruction • Instruction conducted individually or with smaller groups of one to three students with similar needs	• Select units based on your students' areas of need. • Use the units as one component of an intensive comprehension intervention program.

Overview Closed Syllable Pattern

Directions and Sample Answers for Activity Pages

Day 1	See "Model the Skill" below.
Day 2	Read the title and directions aloud. Invite students to divide each word into syllables using the closed syllable pattern. (**bas/ket, cat/nip, traf/fic, sub/tract, hic/cup**) Have students read each word.
Day 3	Read the title and directions aloud. Invite students to sort words into two groups using the closed syllable pattern: double consonants and different consonants. (double consonants: **can/not, at/tract, rab/bit**; different consonants: **hec/tic, cac/tus, sel/dom**) Have students read each word.
Day 4	Read the title and directions aloud. Invite students to locate the six closed syllable words in the story, divide the words into syllables, and read each word to a partner. Assist students who need help dividing the words. (**pic/nic, but/ter, fab/ric, ten/nis, sun/set, con/tent**)
Day 5	Read the directions aloud. Allow time for students to complete the first task. (**bul/let, hus/band, ex/pand, sub/ject**) Next, pronounce the words **jacket**, **cannot**, and **picnic** and ask students to write them on the lines. Afterward, meet individually with students. Ask them to read each word on the assessment page. Discuss their results. Use their responses to plan further instruction and review.

Model the Skill

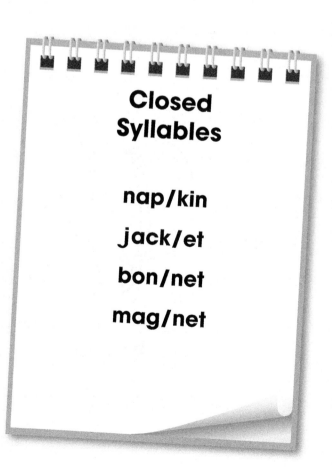

◆ Hand out the Day 1 activity page. Write the word **nap** on the board. Point out that it has one short vowel sound. Have students say the word. **Ask:** *Does this word end with a vowel or a consonant? A consonant. This is an example of a closed syllable.*

◆ **Say:** *You can use what you know about vowel patterns and closed syllables to read longer words. Write the word **napkin** on the first blank of your activity page and follow along as I explain how to divide this word into syllables.* Write the word **napkin** on the board. *First, I circle the two vowels. There are two consonants between the vowels, so I can divide the word between them: **nap/kin**. Copy what I did on your paper.*

◆ Point out that both syllables end with consonants and have a single vowel, so they are both closed syllables. **Say:** *Now I want to read this word. Since vowel sounds in closed syllables are often short, I'll try the short sounds first: /nap/ /kin/, napkin.*

◆ Repeat with **jacket** (**jack/et**). Explain that **c** and **k** together make the consonant digraph that stands for the /**k**/ sound. Explain that you don't divide consonant digraphs.

◆ Then repeat with **bonnet** (**bon/net**), **magnet** (**mag/net**).

Closed Syllables

nap/kin

jack/et

bon/net

mag/net

Closed Syllable Words

Listen to the example. Read each word aloud. Then divide each word into syllables.

napkin

_____

jacket

_____

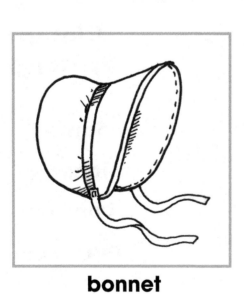

bonnet

_____

magnet

_____

Words Divided

Look at the following words. Divide each word into two closed syllables.
Remember the double letter rule. Then read the words to a partner.

Word List

basket	catnip	traffic	subtract	hiccup

_____

_____

_____

_____

_____

Name _____

Closed Syllable Sort

Sort the following words into two groups using a closed syllable pattern: double consonants or different consonants. Share your results with a partner.

Word List

hectic	cactus	seldom
cannot	attract	rabbit

Double Consonants	Different Consonants

The Picnic

Read the story. Locate the six closed syllable words and write them at the bottom of the page. Divide the words into syllables. Read each word to a partner.

Lisa wanted to go to the park and have a picnic. Her aunt said that was a good idea, so they packed lunch. They packed bread and butter, hard-boiled eggs, fruit, and milk. When they got to the park, they laid a large piece of fabric on the ground. After eating lunch, Lisa and her aunt played tennis. They stayed at the park until sunset. Lisa was very content with her day.

1. _____

2. _____

3. _____

4. _____

5. _____

6. _____

Assessment

Divide the following words into closed syllables.

bullet	husband	expand	subject

_____

_____

_____

_____

Listen to your teacher say each word. Write the words on the lines.

1. _____

2. _____

3. _____

Overview VCe Syllable Pattern

Directions and Sample Answers for Activity Pages

Day 1	See "Model the Skill" below.
Day 2	Read the title and directions aloud. Invite students to divide each word into syllables using the closed and VCe syllable patterns. (**ex/pose, mis/take, in/side, sup/pose, ac/cuse, col/lide, frus/trate, con/crete, ex/plore**) Have students read each word and choose three words to use in sentences.
Day 3	Read the title and directions aloud. Invite students to sort words into three groups using the VCe syllable pattern: double consonants, different consonants, and consonant blends. (double consonants: **op/pose, sap/phire, im/mune**; different consonants: **ex/cuse, com/bine, rep/tile**; consonant blends: **com/plete, cy/clone, in/flate**) Have students read each word.
Day 4	Read the title and directions aloud. Invite students to unscramble the letters in the VCe words and match them to the correct sentences. (**excite, fuse, drape, twine, exhale, episode, plume, slope**)
Day 5	Read the directions aloud. Allow time for students to complete the first task. (**dif/fuse, mem/brane, ig/nite, en/trap, ef/face, in/sane**) Next, pronounce the words **reptile**, **commode**, and **explore** and ask students to write them on the lines. Afterward, meet individually with students. Ask them to read each word on the assessment page. Discuss their results. Use their responses to plan further instruction and review.

Model the Skill

◆ Hand out the Day 1 activity page. Write **pole** on the board and read it aloud. Model blending the onset and rime: **/pōl/, pole. Say:** *Notice that this word has one syllable, one vowel sound, and a VCe pattern. You can use what you know about vowel patterns and syllables to read longer words.*

◆ Write **tadpole** on the board. **Say:** *Notice the silent final* **e** *and the other two vowels in this word.* Circle the vowels **a** and **o**. **Ask:** *How many consonants do you see between these two vowels? I will try dividing the word between the two consonants:* **tad/pole**. Point out that the first syllable is a closed syllable and the second syllable has a VCe pattern.

◆ **Say:** *Now I want to read this word. Since vowel sounds in closed syllables are often short, I'll try the short sound for the first syllable. Since vowel sounds in VCe patterns are often long, I'll try the long vowel sound for the second syllable.* Model reading the two parts of the word and blending them together: **/tad/ /pōl/, tadpole.**

◆ Repeat with **commode** (**com/mode**) and **explode** (**ex/plode**).

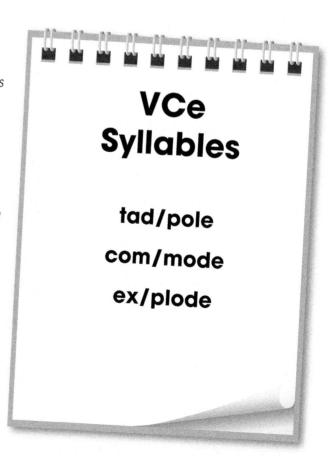

VCe
Syllables

tad/pole

com/mode

ex/plode

VCe Syllables

Listen to the example. Read each word aloud. Then divide each word into two syllables.

tadpole

_____

commode

_____

explode

_____

Words Divided

Look at the following words. Divide each word into two syllables. Remember that one syllable is closed and the other syllable has a VCe pattern. Then read the words to a partner.

List 1:	List 2:	List 3:
expose	suppose	frustrate
mistake	accuse	concrete
inside	collide	explore

Choose one word from each list to use in a sentence.

1. _____

_____

2. _____

_____

3. _____

_____

Name _____

VCe Syllable Sort

Sort the following words into three groups using a VCe syllable pattern: double consonants, different consonants, or consonant blends. Share your results with a partner.

Word List

complete	oppose	excuse
combine	reptile	cyclone
inflate	sapphire	immune

Double Consonants	Different Consonants	Consonant Blends

Unit 2 • *Everyday Phonics Intervention Activities Grade 4* • © Newmark Learning, LLC

VCe Word Scramble

Unscramble the VCe words and write them in the blank in the correct sentence.

xalhee	**cteixe**	**plseo**	**uesf**
praed	**wetni**	**speidoe**	**uepml**

It's almost time for bed, so don't _____ yourself.

If the lights go out, check the _____ box.

_____ this blanket over your shoulders. You look like you are cold.

You can use _____, or rope, to tie the package.

Take a deep breath and inhale. Let the breath out while you
_____.

My mom let me watch the latest _____ of *Superman* on TV.

That clown looks so funny with that ostrich _____ in his hat.

Don't fall down the _____. It's a long way to the bottom.

Name _____

Assessment

Divide the following words into closed and VCe syllable patterns.

diffuse	membrane	ignite	entrap	efface	insane

Listen to your teacher say each word. Write the words on the lines.

1. _____

2. _____

3. _____

Overview Open Syllable Pattern

Directions and Sample Answers for Activity Pages

Day 1	See "Model the Skill" below.
Day 2	Read the title and directions aloud. Have students read each word. Then invite students to divide each word into syllables using the open syllable pattern. (**ro/dent, hu/man, u/nit, a/gent, so/lo, e/go, cra/zy, ti/dy**) Then have students choose three words to use in a sentence.
Day 3	Read the title and directions aloud. Invite students to sort words into two groups: open/closed syllable patterns and open/open syllable patterns. (open/closed: **ro/bot, si/ren, si/lent, to/tem**; open/open: **sha/ky, si/lo, la/zy, ha/lo**) Have students share results with a partner.
Day 4	Read the title and directions aloud. Invite students to divide the words into open and closed syllables. Then have students locate the words in the word search. (**so/lid, rhi/no, ru/by, hu/mid, o/pen, fo/cus**)
Day 5	Read the directions aloud. Allow time for students to complete the first task. (**mo/ment, i/tem, pho/to, to/tal, ba/by**) Next, pronounce the words **unit**, **solo**, and **lazy** and ask students to write them on the lines. Afterward, meet individually with students. Ask them to read each word on the assessment page. Discuss their results. Use their responses to plan further instruction and review.

Model the Skill

◆ Hand out the Day 1 activity page. Write **go** and **shy** on the board and ask students to say the words. Point out that each word has one vowel sound, so it is a one-syllable word. Then point out that each word ends in a vowel. **Say:** *A syllable that ends in a vowel is an open syllable. You can use what you know about letter patterns and open syllables to read longer words.*

◆ Write **music** on the board. **Say:** *I will circle the two vowels. Notice the single consonant between the two vowels. When there is one consonant, try dividing the word before the consonant: **mu/sic**. Copy what I did on your paper.* Point out that the first syllable ends with a vowel, so it is an open syllable.

◆ **Say:** *Now I want to read this word. Since vowel sounds in open syllables are often long, I'll try the long sound first.* Model reading the two parts of the word and blending them together: **/mu/ /sic/**, **music**. Remind students that **/sic/** is a closed syllable so they should try a short vowel sound for it.

◆ Repeat with the remaining words. Point out that **music** and **program** are made up of open and closed patterns, and **gravy** and **solo** are made of two open patterns (**pro/gram, gra/vy, so/lo**).

Open Syllables

mu/sic

pro/gram

gra/vy

so/lo

Open Syllables

Use what you know about open and closed syllable patterns to divide these words.

music

_____

program

_____

gravy

_____

solo

_____

Name _____

Words Divided

Read the following words. Divide each word into two syllables. Remember that some words have only open syllable patterns while other words have open and closed syllable patterns.

List 1:	List 2:
rodent	solo
human	ego
unit	crazy
agent	tidy

Choose three words from the list to use in a sentence.

1. _____

   _____

2. _____

   _____

3. _____

   _____

Syllable Pattern Sort

Sort the following words into two categories: open/closed syllable patterns and open/open syllable patterns. Share your results with a partner.

Word List

robot	silo	lazy	silent
shaky	siren	halo	totem

Open/Closed	Open/Open

Name _____

Word Search

Divide the words into open and closed syllables. Then locate the words in the word search.

| solid | rhino | ruby | humid | open | focus |

s	u	c	o	f	c	s
z	d	i	m	u	h	r
d	o	a	n	x	d	u
r	h	i	n	o	t	b
w	a	z	v	o	b	y
d	i	l	o	s	t	t
e	n	e	p	o	y	s

Assessment

Divide the following words into syllables. Underline each open syllable.

moment	item	photo	total	baby

Listen to your teacher say each word. Write the words on the lines.

1. _____

2. _____

3. _____

UNIT 4

Overview Long a Digraph Syllable Pattern

Directions and Sample Answers for Activity Pages

Day 1	See "Model the Skill" below.
Day 2	Read the title and directions aloud. Invite students to divide each word into syllables using open, closed, and long **a** digraph syllable patterns. (**mer/maid, ex/plain, de/lay, a/way, beef/steak, great/er, weigh/ty, freight/er, sur/vey, grey/hound**) Have students read each word and choose three words to use in sentences.
Day 3	Read the title and directions aloud. Invite students to sort words into groups using the long **a** digraph syllable pattern: **ai, ay, ea, ei, ey**. (**ai: trail, detail, contain; ay: relay, display, stray; ea: great, steak, newsbreak; ei: neigh, sleigh, vein; ey: prey, disobey, whey**) Have students read each word.
Day 4	Read the title and directions aloud. Invite students to locate the fourteen long **a** digraph syllable words in the story. Have them read each word to a partner. (**rain, away, day, complained, Hey, bait, great, weighed, paid, bay, break, eight, they, rainy**)
Day 5	Read the directions aloud. Allow time for students to complete the first task. (**re/main, hoo/ray, heart/break, weight/less, con/vey**) Next, pronounce the words **mermaid, display, greater, vein**, and **survey** and ask students to write them on the lines. Afterward, meet individually with students. Ask them to read each word on the assessment page. Discuss their results. Use their responses to plan further instruction and review.

Model the Skill

◆ Hand out the Day 1 activity page. Write **day** on the board and ask students to say the word. Point out that **day** has one open syllable and one long vowel sound. **Say:** *Ay is another way to make the long **a** sound. You can use what you know about letter patterns and syllables to read longer words.*

◆ Write **daybreak** on the board. **Say:** *I will circle the vowels **ay** and **ea**. Both **ay** and **ea** make the long **a** sound. There are two consonants between the vowels, but I notice that the consonants are **b** and **r**, which is a consonant blend that makes the **/br/** sound. I can't divide between a blend, so I'll divide between the **/y/** and **/b/**: **day/break**.* Copy what I did on your paper. Point out that the second syllable ends in a consonant, so it is a closed syllable.

◆ **Say:** *Now I want to read this word. Since both syllables have long **a** digraphs, I'll try the long sound first for both syllables.* Model reading the two parts of the word and blending them together: **/d/ /ā/ /br/ /ā/ /k/, daybreak.**

◆ Explain that the long **a** digraph sound can also be made with **ai, ey**, and **ei**, as in **raisin, obey, veil, eight**, and **reign**.

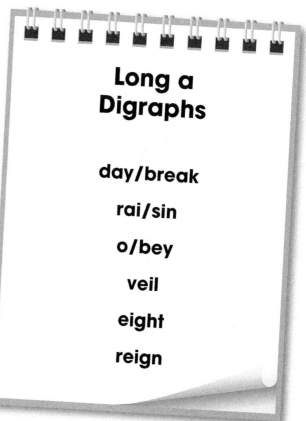

Long a Digraphs

day/break

rai/sin

o/bey

veil

eight

reign

Name _____

Long a Digraphs

Divide these words into syllables where applicable.
Then circle the long *a* sound in each word, as in *say*.

daybreak

raisin

_____

obey

_____

veil

_____

eight

_____

reign

_____

Unit 4 • Everyday Phonics Intervention Activities Grade 4 • © Newmark Learning, LLC

Words Divided

Look at the following words. Divide each word into syllables using closed, open, and long *a* digraphs. Then read the words to a partner.

List 1:	List 2:	List 3:	List 4:	List 5:
mermaid explain	delay away	beefsteak greater	weighty freighter	survey greyhound

Choose three words to use in sentences.

1. _____

   _____

2. _____

   _____

3. _____

   _____

Name _____

Long a Digraph Syllable Sort

Sort the following words into groups using the long *a* digraph syllable pattern: *ai*, *ay*, *ea*, *ei*, and *ey*. Share your results with a partner.

Word List

stray	steak	contain	relay	whey
trail	neigh	disobey	display	great
prey	detail	newsbreak	sleigh	vein

ai	ay	ea	ei	ey

Fishing in the Rain

Read the story. Locate the fourteen long *a* digraph syllable words and write them at the bottom of the page. Read each word to a partner.

"Rain, go away. Come again some other day," Jack sang.

"This will never stop," complained Tim. "And I'm tired of being indoors."

"Hey!" yelled Jack. "Let's buy some bait and go fishing."

"That's a great idea," replied Tim.

Tim and Jack took their poles, a bucket, and some money and ran down to the local fishing store. The boys weighed one pound of worms on the scale, paid the shopkeeper, and walked to the bay.

The boys fished for hours before finally catching a break. By sunset, Jack and Tim had caught eight large bluefish . . . more than they had ever caught before.

"Rainy days aren't so bad after all," Tim said.

1. _____   8. _____

2. _____   9. _____

3. _____   10. _____

4. _____   11. _____

5. _____   12. _____

6. _____   13. _____

7. _____   14. _____

Assessment

Divide the following words into syllables.

remain	hooray	heartbreak	weightless	convey

Listen to your teacher say each word. Write the words on the lines.

1. _____

2. _____

3. _____

4. _____

5. _____

Overview Long o Digraph Syllable Pattern

Directions and Sample Answers for Activity Pages

Day 1	See "Model the Skill" below.
Day 2	Read the title and directions aloud. Invite students to divide each word into syllables using open, closed, and long **o** digraph syllable patterns. (**over/coat, a/float, char/coal, mistle/toe, tippy/toe, a/glow, over/flow, rain/bow**) Have students read each word and choose three words to use in sentences.
Day 3	Read the title and directions aloud. Invite students to sort words into groups using the long **o** digraph syllable pattern: **oa**, **oe**, and **ow**. (**oa: reproach, croak, coast; oe: foe, hoe, woe; ow: stow, undertow, know**) Have students read each word.
Day 4	Read the title and directions aloud. Invite students to cut out the sentence parts and then put the parts together to form sentences that make sense. Have students glue correctly formed sentences on a piece of notebook paper. (A cockroach ran under the fridge. My mother decorates the house with mistletoe. I need to hoe the weeds in the garden. Every Saturday, I have to mow the grass. I saw a huge truckload of pigs on the highway. I just saw a fawn, so a doe must be close. The cornfield had a huge scarecrow standing in it. When in deep water, try to stay afloat. An undertow can pull you away from the shore.)
Day 5	Read the directions aloud. Allow time for students to complete the first task. (**over/coat, char/coal, mistle/toe, tippy/toe, rain/bow, slide/show**). Next, pronounce the words **foal**, **doe**, and **outgrow** and ask students to write them on the lines. Afterward, meet individually with students. Ask them to read each word on the assessment page. Discuss their results. Use their responses to plan further instruction and review.

Model the Skill

◆ Hand out the Day 1 activity page. Write **toast** on the board and ask students to say the word. Point out that **toast** has one closed syllable and one long vowel sound. **Say:** *Oa is another way to make the long **o** sound. You can use what you know about letter patterns and syllables to read longer words.*

◆ Write **toasted** on the board. **Say:** *I will circle the vowels **oa** and **e**. There are two consonants between the vowels, but in this word the **s** and **t** make the consonant blend **/st/**. We do not separate consonant blends, so I'll divide the word after the **t**: toast/ed.*

◆ **Say:** *Now I want to read this word. The first syllable is closed so I could make the short vowel sound, but I also know the **/oa/** makes the long **o** sound so I'll try that first. The second syllable is also a closed syllable, so I'll try the short vowel sound first.* Model reading the two parts of the word and blending them together: **/t/ /ōst/ /ed/, toasted**.

◆ Explain that the long **o** digraph sound can also be made with **ow** and **oe**, as in **below** and **toenail**.

Long o Digraphs

toast/ed

be/low

toe/nail

Long o Digraphs

Divide these words into syllables. Then circle the long *o* sound in each word.

toasted

_____

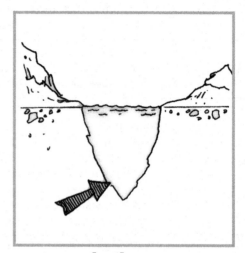

below

_____

toenail

_____

Words Divided

Look at the following words. Divide each word into syllables using closed, open, and long *o* digraphs. Then read the words to a partner.

List 1:	List 2:	List 3:
overcoat	mistletoe	aglow
afloat	tippy-toe	overflow
charcoal		rainbow

Choose three words to use in sentences.

1. _____

_____

2. _____

_____

3. _____

_____

Long o Digraph Syllable Sort

Sort the following words into groups using the long *o* digraph syllable pattern: *oa, oe,* and *ow*. Share your results with a partner.

Word List

undertow	foe	woe
hoe	reproach	coast
croak	know	stow

oa	oe	ow

Sentence Scramble

Cut out the sentence parts and then put the parts together to form sentences that make sense. Glue correctly formed sentences on a piece of notebook paper. Read the sentences to a partner.

A cockroach ran	mow the grass.
My mother decorates	try to stay afloat.
I need to hoe	so a doe must be close.
Every Saturday, I have to	the house with mistletoe.
I saw a huge truckload	huge scarecrow standing in it.
I just saw a fawn,	under the fridge.
The cornfield had a	of pigs on the highway.
When in deep water,	pull you away from the shore.
An undertow can	the weeds in the garden.

Assessment

Divide the following words into syllables.

overcoat	**mistletoe**	**rainbow**
charcoal	**tippy-toe**	**slideshow**

Listen to your teacher say each word. Write the words on the lines.

1. _____

2. _____

3. _____

Overview Long e Digraph Syllable Pattern

Directions and Sample Answers for Activity Pages

Day 1	See "Model the Skill" below.
Day 2	Read the title and directions aloud. Invite students to divide each word into syllables using open, closed, and long **e** digraph syllable patterns. (**re/lease, mis/treat, re/peat, es/teem, cof/fee, a/gree, don/key, gal/ley, val/ley, hair/piece, de/brief, be/lief**) Have students read each word and choose three words to use in sentences.
Day 3	Read the title and directions aloud. Invite students to sort words into groups using the long **e** digraph syllable pattern: **ea, ee, ey,** and **ie**. (**ea: reason, peanut; ee: canteen, between; ey: key, volley; ie: relief, thief**) Have students read each word.
Day 4	Read the title and directions aloud. Invite students to divide the long **e** digraph words into open and closed syllables. Then have students locate the words in the word search. (**de/feat, mis/treat, thir/teen, pro/ceed, mon/key, don/key, a/piece, de/brief**)
Day 5	Read the directions aloud. Allow time for students to complete the first task. (**con/ceal, mis/lead, em/cee, dis/creet, gal/ley, val/ley, time/piece, re/lief**). Next, pronounce the words **reason, canteen, donkey,** and **thief** and ask students to write them on the lines. Afterward, meet individually with students. Ask them to read each word on the assessment page. Discuss their results. Use their responses to plan further instruction and review.

Model the Skill

Long e Digraphs

steam

be/neath

mon/key

re/lief

◆ Hand out the Day 1 activity page. Write **steam** on the board and ask students to say the word. Point out that **steam** has one closed syllable and one long vowel sound. Have students circle **ea** on their activity page. **Say:** *Ea is another way to make the long* **e** *sound. You can use what you know about letter patterns and syllables to read longer words.*

◆ Write **beneath** on the board. **Say:** *I will circle the vowels* **e** *and* **ea**. *There is one consonant between them, so I'll divide the word before the consonant:* **be/neath**. *Copy what I did on your paper.*

◆ **Say:** *Now I want to read this word. The first syllable is open so I'll try a long vowel sound first. The second syllable is a closed syllable. I know closed syllables often have a short vowel sound, but I also know that* **ea** *makes the long* **e** *sound, so for the second syllable I'll try the long* **e** *sound first.* Model reading the two parts of the word and blending them together: **/b/ /ē/ /n/ /ē/ /th/, beneath**.

◆ Explain that the long **e** digraph sound can also be made with **ey** and **ie** as in **monkey** and **relief**. Point out open and closed syllables.

Long e Digraphs

Divide the following words into syllables where applicable. Then circle the long *e* sound in each word.

steam

_____

beneath

_____

monkey

_____

relief

_____

Words Divided

Look at the following words. Divide each word into syllables using closed, open, and long e digraphs. Then read the words to a partner.

List 1:	List 2:	List 3:	List 4:
release	esteem	donkey	hairpiece
mistreat	coffee	galley	debrief
repeat	agree	valley	belief

Choose three words to use in sentences.

1. _____

_____

2. _____

_____

3. _____

_____

Word Search

Sort the following words into groups using the long *e* digraph syllable pattern: *ea*, *ee*, *ey*, and *ie*. Share your results with a partner.

Word List

relief	**volley**	**thief**	**key**
reason	**between**	**peanut**	**canteen**

ea	ee	ey	ie

Word Search

Divide the long *e* digraph words into open and closed syllables.
Then locate the words in the word search.

| defeat | mistreat | thirteen | proceed |
| monkey | donkey | apiece | debrief |

m	i	s	t	r	e	a	t
n	e	e	t	r	i	h	t
f	v	d	o	n	k	e	y
e	o	e	d	w	g	n	l
i	d	e	f	e	a	t	a
r	i	c	k	z	z	h	u
b	m	o	n	k	e	y	g
e	x	r	b	q	t	o	h
d	a	p	i	e	c	e	m

Assessment

Divide the following words into syllables.

conceal	mislead	emcee	discreet
galley	valley	timepiece	relief

Listen to your teacher say each word. Write the words on the lines.

1. _____

2. _____

3. _____

4. _____

Overview Long i Digraph Syllable Pattern

Directions and Sample Answers for Activity Pages

Day 1	See "Model the Skill" below.
Day 2	Read the title and directions aloud. Invite students to divide each word into syllables using open, closed, and long **i** digraph syllable patterns. (**mag/pie, de/fied, sup/plies, re/plied, de/light, twi/light, high/way, night/ly**) Have students read each word and choose three words to use in sentences.
Day 3	Read the title and directions aloud. Invite students to sort words into groups using the long **i** digraph syllable pattern: **ie** and **igh**. (**ie: relies, vie, denied, untied**; **igh: bright, bullfight, lightly, eyesight**) Have students read each word.
Day 4	Read the title and directions aloud. Invite students to locate the seven long **i** digraph syllable words in the story. Read each word to a partner. (**notified, replied, applied, terrified, might, highlight, right**)
Day 5	Read the directions aloud. Allow time for students to complete the first task. (**sup/plied, un/tie, im/plies, day/light, fright/en, right/ly**) Next, pronounce the words **applied**, **magpie**, **delight**, and **twilight** and ask students to write them on the lines. Afterward, meet individually with students. Ask them to read each word on the assessment page. Discuss their results. Use their responses to plan further instruction and review.

Model the Skill

Long i Digraphs

pie

neck/tie

light/ning

◆ Hand out the Day 1 activity page. Write **pie** on the board and ask students to say the word. Point out that **pie** has one open syllable and one long vowel sound. Have students circle **ie** on their activity page. **Say:** *ie is another way to make the long i sound. You can use what you know about letter patterns and syllables to read longer words.*

◆ Write **necktie** on the board. **Say:** *I will circle the vowels e and ie. We see one consonant digraph ck and one consonant t between the vowels. Digraphs should not be divided, so I'll divide the word after the consonant digraph: neck/tie. Copy what I did on your paper.*

◆ **Say:** *Now I want to read this word. The first syllable is a closed syllable, so I'll try a short vowel sound first. The second syllable is an open syllable. I know open syllables often make the long vowel sound. I also know /ie/ makes the long i sound, so I'll make the long vowel sound first.* Model reading the two parts of the word and blending them together: **/nek/ /t/ /ī/, necktie.**

◆ Explain that the long **i** sound can also be made with **igh** as in **lightning**. (**light/ning**) Point out that the first syllable is closed, but **/igh/** makes the long **i** sound. The second syllable is also closed.

Long i Digraphs

Divide the following words into syllables where applicable.
Then circle the long *i* sound in each word.

pie

_____

necktie

_____

lightning

_____

Words Divided

Look at the following words. Divide each word into syllables using closed, open, and long *i* digraphs. Then read the words to a partner.

List 1:	List 2:
magpie	delight
defied	twilight
supplies	highway
replied	nightly

Choose three words to use in sentences.

1. _____

_____

2. _____

_____

3. _____

_____

Long i Digraph Syllable Sort

Sort the following words into groups using the long *i* digraph syllable pattern: *ie* and *igh*. Share your results with a partner.

Word List

relies	bullfight	untied	lightly
eyesight	denied	bright	vie

ie	igh

Cowboy Camp

Read the story. Locate the seven long _i_ digraph syllable words and write them at the bottom of the page. Read each word to a partner.

"I can't believe this," said Chris after he read the letter addressed to him. "I've been notified about Cowboy Camp. I'm accepted."

"Wow!" replied Steve. "I've applied to Cowboy Camp for two years and haven't been accepted yet. How'd you get in?"

"I'm not sure, but let's go over to your house and see if you got a letter, too," Chris said.

The boys ran two houses down the street, flew through the front door, and asked Steve's mom if he'd received a letter from Cowboy Camp.

"You bet you did," Steve's mom answered. "Open it and tell us what it says."

"You read it for me, Mom," Steve whispered. "I'm terrified of what the letter might say."

"OK," she whispered back.

Steve's mom read the letter, which said that Steve was accepted to this summer's Cowboy Camp. Steve and Chris jumped up and down with pure joy. They would get to attend camp together for the first time.

"This summer is going to be the highlight of the year," Chris squealed. "Let's think about what we want to take with us."

"Right now," Steve's mom said with her stern voice, "it's time for Steve to clean his room. Are you staying to help, Chris?"

"See you later, Steve," Chris yelled as he was halfway out the front door.

1. _____   5. _____

2. _____   6. _____

3. _____   7. _____

4. _____

Name _____

Assessment

Divide the following words into syllables.

supplied	**untie**	**implies**
daylight	**frighten**	**rightly**

Listen to your teacher say each word. Write the words on the lines.

1. _____

2. _____

3. _____

4. _____

Overview r-Controlled a Syllable Pattern

Directions and Sample Answers for Activity Pages

Day 1	See "Model the Skill" below.
Day 2	Read the title and directions aloud. Invite students to divide each word into syllables using open, closed, and **r**-controlled **a** syllable patterns. (**gar/lic, tar/get, par/don, mar/ket, gui/tar, a/jar, re/mark, aard/vark**) Have students read each word and choose three words to use in sentences.
Day 3	Read the title and directions aloud. Invite students to sort words into groups using the **r**-controlled **a** syllable pattern: **r**-controlled **a** in first syllable and **r**-controlled **a** in second syllable. (first syllable: **marshal, varnish, arson, scarlet**; second syllable: **regard, jaguar, discard, discharge**) Have students read each word.
Day 4	Read the title and directions aloud. Invite students to unscramble the sentences and write them on the lines. Then have students draw a picture that shows what is happening in each sentence. Have them read each sentence to a partner. (The hay harvest is in the barn. I got a charm at the market. The card had a starry night on it. Why is a harp in the garden?)
Day 5	Read the directions aloud. Allow time for students to complete the first task. (**jar/gon, char/ter, char/coal, a/part, dis/arm, bom/bard**) Next, pronounce the words **garlic, arson, remark**, and **ajar** and ask students to write them on the lines. Afterward, meet individually with students. Ask them to read each word on the assessment page. Discuss their results. Use their responses to plan further instruction and review.

Model the Skill

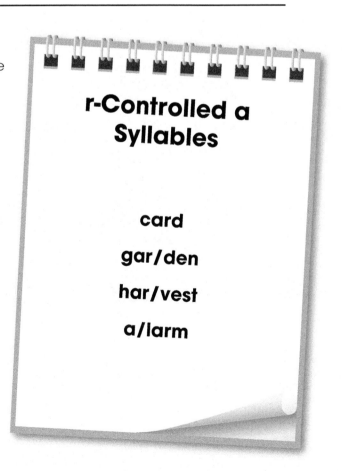

r-Controlled a Syllables

card

gar/den

har/vest

a/larm

◆ Hand out the Day 1 activity page. Write **card** on the board and ask students to say the word. Point out that **card** has one closed syllable. Have students circle the **ar**. **Say:** *The letters **ar** in the middle of **card** sound like **are**. The vowel sound is neither long nor short. When the letter **r** follows a vowel, it affects, or controls, the sound that the vowel stands for. These syllables are called **r**-controlled.*

◆ Write **garden** on the board. **Say:** *I will circle the vowels **a** and **e**. When words with **r**-controlled vowels are divided into syllables, the vowel and the **r** usually stay in the same syllable. I'll divide the word between the consonants: **gar/den**. Copy what I did on your paper.*

◆ **Say:** *Now I want to read this word. The first syllable is closed, but it is also **r**-controlled. I think this syllable should sound like /är/ as in **are**. The second syllable is also closed. I know closed syllables often make the short vowel sound, so I'll try the short vowel sound first.* Model reading the two parts of the word and blending them together: /gär/ /den/, **garden**. Repeat with **harvest** and **alarm**.

Name _____

r-Controlled a Syllables

**Divide the following words into syllables where applicable.
Then circle the *r*-controlled sound in each word.**

card

_____

garden

_____

harvest

_____

alarm

_____

Words Divided

Look at the following words. Divide each word into syllables using closed, open, and *r*-controlled *a* syllables. Then read the words to a partner.

List 1:	List 2:
garlic	guitar
target	ajar
pardon	remark
market	aardvark

Choose three words to use in sentences.

1. _____

_____

2. _____

_____

3. _____

_____

r-Controlled a Syllable Sort

Sort the following words into groups using the *r*-controlled *a* syllable pattern: *r*-controlled *a* in the first syllable and *r*-controlled *a* in the second syllable. Share your results with a partner.

Word List:

regard	varnish	marshal	scarlet
arson	discard	jaguar	discharge

r-controlled a first syllable	r-controlled a second syllable

Sentence Scramble

Unscramble the sentences and write them on the lines. Then draw a picture that shows what is happening in each sentence. Read your sentences to a partner.

the hay is barn in The harvest

_____

_____

market I a the at charm got

_____

_____

starry card The on a it night had

_____

_____

harp is in garden Why the a

_____

_____

Assessment

Divide the following words into syllables.

jargon	**charter**	**charcoal**
apart	**disarm**	**bombard**

Listen to your teacher say each word. Write the words on the lines.

1. _____

2. _____

3. _____

4. _____

Overview r-Controlled o Syllable Pattern

Directions and Sample Answers for Activity Pages

Day 1	See "Model the Skill" below.
Day 2	Read the title and directions aloud. Invite students to divide each word into syllables using open, closed, and **r**-controlled **o** syllable patterns. (**ga/lore, chor/us, hoard/ing, up/roar, in/door, floor/boards, re/source, down/pour.** The word **floorboards** has **oo** and **oa** in it.) Have students read each word and choose three words to use in sentences.
Day 3	Read the title and directions aloud. Invite students to sort words into groups using the **r**-controlled **o** syllable pattern: **or, oar, oor,** and **our** (**or: floral, before; oar: soaring, boar; oor: outdoor, floor; our: fourteen, pour**) Have students read each word.
Day 4	Read the title and directions aloud. Invite students to locate the eight **r**-controlled **o** syllable words in the story. Read each word to a partner. (**your, board, outdoors, storm, downpour, roaring, floor, ignore**)
Day 5	Read the directions aloud. Allow time for students to complete the first task. (**hor/net, im/port, up/roar, a/board, in/door, trap/door, re/source, four/teen**) Next, pronounce the words **floral**, **soaring**, **floor**, and **pour** and ask students to write them on the lines. Afterward, meet individually with students. Ask them to read each word on the assessment page. Discuss their results. Use their responses to plan further instruction and review.

Model the Skill

◆ Hand out the Day 1 activity page. Write **fork** on the board and ask students to say the word. Point out that **fork** has one closed syllable. Have students circle **or.** **Say:** *The letters **or** in the middle of **fork** sound like **or.** The vowel sound is neither long nor short. When the letter **r** follows a vowel, it affects, or controls, the sound that the vowel stands for. These syllables are called **r**-controlled. You can use what you know about letter patterns and syllables to read longer words.*

◆ Write **snorkel** on the board. **Say:** *I will circle the vowels **o** and **e.** When words with **r**-controlled vowels are divided into syllables, the vowel and the **r** usually stay in the same syllable. I'll divide the word between the **r** and **k**: **snor/kel.** Copy what I did on your paper.*

◆ **Say:** *Now I want to read this word. The first syllable is closed, but it is also **r**-controlled. I think this syllable should sound like **/or/** as in **or.** The second syllable is also closed. I know closed syllables often make the short vowel sound, so I'll try the short vowel sound first.* Model reading the two parts of the word and blending them together: **/sn/ /or/ /kel/, snorkel.**

◆ Repeat with **our, oar, oor,** as in **fourteen, aboard,** and **trapdoor.**

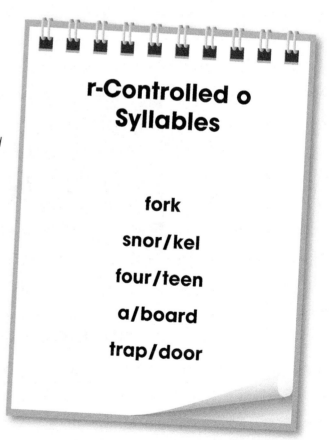

r-Controlled o Syllables

fork

snor/kel

four/teen

a/board

trap/door

Name _____

r-Controlled o Syllables

**Divide the following words into syllables where applicable.
Then circle the *r*-controlled sound in each word.**

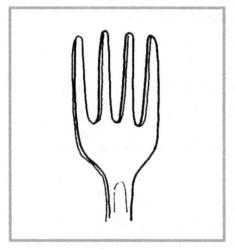

fork

_____

snorkel

_____

fourteen

_____

aboard

_____

trapdoor

_____

Words Divided

Look at the following words. Divide each word into syllables using closed, open, and *r*-controlled *o* syllables. Then read the words to a partner.

List 1:	List 2:	List 3:	List 4:
galore	hoarding	indoor	resource
chorus	uproar	floorboards	downpour

Choose three words to use in sentences.

1. _____

_____

2. _____

_____

3. _____

_____

What is unusual about the word *floorboards*?

_____

_____

Name _____

r-Controlled o Syllable Sort

Sort the following words into groups using the *r*-controlled *o* syllable pattern: *or, oar, oor,* and *our*. Share your results with a partner.

Word List

outdoor	before	soaring	pour
boar	fourteen	floral	floor

or	oar	oor	our

Not the Best Halloween Ever!

Read the story. Locate the eight *r*-controlled *o* syllable words and write them at the bottom of the page. Divide each word into syllables and read each word to a partner.

"I can't believe we're stuck out here," Alex whined. "We're going to miss the Halloween party. All because your car ran over a board and got a flat tire. And your spare has a flat, too."

"Hey," replied Jamie. "We're outdoors on Halloween night. It's spooky. This is great. What else could go wrong?"

At just that moment, a storm broke. A downpour with roaring wind overtook the boys.

"Okay," Jamie said. "Something else could go wrong. Let's get back in the car, and I'll call my parents on my cell phone."

Jamie reached for his cell phone and realized that he didn't have it. "Where's my cell?" screamed Jamie.

"Calm down," Alex said. "It's got to be here somewhere. Look. Here it is on the floor. Now make the call."

Jamie called his parents, told them what happened, and asked his dad to bring a spare tire. Fifteen minutes later, his parents arrived. Jamie and Alex changed the tire in the rain, and soon they were on their way home.

The next day, Jamie's dad said, "Maybe the next time I tell you to check the spare, you won't ignore me."

"I don't think I'm ever going to drive again," stated Jamie.

1. _____   5. _____

2. _____   6. _____

3. _____   7. _____

4. _____   8. _____

Name _____

Assessment

Divide the following words into syllables.

hornet	import	uproar	aboard
indoor	trapdoor	resource	fourteen

Listen to your teacher say each word. Write the words on the lines.

1. _____

2. _____

3. _____

4. _____

UNIT 10

Overview r-Controlled e, i, and u Syllable Pattern

Directions and Sample Answers for Activity Pages

Day 1	See "Model the Skill" below.
Day 2	Read the title and directions aloud. Invite students to divide each word into syllables using open, closed, and r-controlled **e, i,** and **u** syllable patterns. (**toast/er, pro/verb, ob/serve, twirl/ing, a/whirl, quirk/y, sub/urb, sur/prise, oc/cur**) Have students read each word and choose three words to use in sentences.
Day 3	Read the title and directions aloud. Invite students to sort words into groups using the r-controlled **e, i,** and **u** syllable patterns: (**er: superb, submerge, verge; ir: astir, lovebird, whirl; ur: disturb, sunburn, curse**) Have students read each word.
Day 4	Read the title and directions aloud. Invite students to complete the crossword puzzle using the clues and words in the box. (Across: 4. **berserk**, 5. **whirl**, 6. **alter**; Down: 1. **concern**, 2. **toaster**, 3. **headfirst**)
Day 5	Read the directions aloud. Allow time for students to complete the first task. (**ad/verb, in/tern, quirk/y, song/bird, noc/turne, re/turn**) Next, pronounce the words **observe**, **whirl**, and **disturb** and ask students to write them on the lines. Afterward, meet individually with students. Ask them to read each word on the assessment page. Discuss their results. Use their responses to plan further instruction and review.

Model the Skill

◆ Hand out the Day 1 activity page. Write **dirt** on the board and ask students to say the word. Point out that **dirt** has one closed syllable. Have students circle **ir**. **Say:** *The letters **ir** in the middle of **dirt** sound like **fur**. The vowel sound is neither long nor short. When the letter **r** follows a vowel, it affects, or controls, the sound that the vowel stands for. These syllables are called r-controlled.*

◆ Write **dirty** on the board. **Say:** *I will circle the vowels **i** and **y**. When words with r-controlled vowels are divided into syllables, the vowel and the **r** usually stay in the same syllable. The **t** is a part of the word **dirt** so I can't divide between the **r** and **t**. I'll divide the word between the **t** and **y**: **dirt/y**.*

◆ **Say:** *Now I want to read this word. The first syllable is closed, but it is also r-controlled. I think this syllable should sound like **/ûr/** as in **fur**. The second syllable is open and is a single **y**. I know open syllables with a single **y** often make the long vowel sound, so I'll try the long vowel sound first. Model reading the two parts of the word and blending them together: **/dûrt/ /ē/, dirty**. Repeat with **er** and **ur** as in **merchant** and **turkey**.*

r-controlled e, i, u syllables

dirt

dirty

mer/chant

tur/key

Unit 10 • Everyday Phonics Intervention Activities Grade 4 • © Newmark Learning, LLC

55

r-Controlled i, e, u Syllables

Divide the following words into syllables where applicable.
Then circle the *r*-controlled sound in each word.

dirt

_____

dirty

_____

merchant

_____

turkey

_____

Words Divided

Look at the following words. Divide each word into syllables using closed, open, and *r*-controlled *e, i,* and *u* syllables. Then read the words to a partner.

List 1:	List 2:	List 3:
toaster	twirling	suburb
proverb	awhirl	surprise
observe	quirky	occur

Choose three words to use in sentences.

1. _____

_____

2. _____

_____

3. _____

_____

r-Controlled e, i, and u Syllable Sort

Sort the following words into groups using the *r-controlled e, i,* and *u* syllable pattern: *er, ir,* and *ur*. Share your results with a partner.

Word List

astir	whirl	curse
sunburn	superb	submerge
verge	disturb	lovebird

er	ir	ur

Crossword Puzzle

Complete the crossword puzzle using the clues and the words in the box.

concern	whirl	headfirst	berserk	alter	toaster

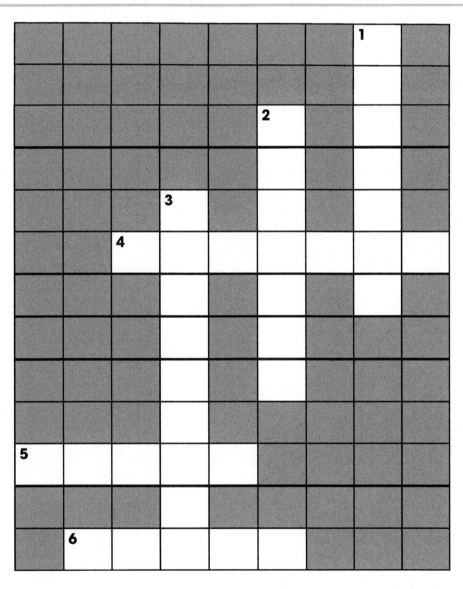

CLUES

Across

4. crazy
5. to move around and around
6. to change

Down

1. worry
2. a machine that browns bread
3. moving forward with your head

Assessment

Divide the following words into syllables.

adverb	intern	quirky	songbird	nocturne	return

Listen to your teacher say each word. Write the words on the lines.

1. _____

2. _____

3. _____

Overview r-Controlled /âr/ Syllable Pattern

Directions and Sample Answers for Activity Pages

Day 1	See "Model the Skill" below.
Day 2	Read the title and directions aloud. Invite students to divide each word into syllables using open, closed, and **r**-controlled **/âr/** syllable patterns. (**hair/y, de/spair, wear/ing, swim/wear, be/ware, pre/pare**) Have students read each word and choose three words to use in sentences.
Day 3	Read the title and directions aloud. Invite students to sort words into groups using the **r**-controlled **/âr/** syllable patterns. (**air: impair, midair, dairy; ear: pear, tear; are: fanfare, compare, mare**) Have students read each word.
Day 4	Read the title and directions aloud. Invite students to locate the six **r**-controlled **/âr/** syllable words in the story. Read each word to a partner. (**fair, square, unaware, teddy bear, pears, affair**)
Day 5	Read the directions aloud. Allow time for students to complete the first task. (**re/pair, stair/case, tear/ing, bear/skin, de/clare, night/mare**) Next, pronounce the words **hairy**, **wearing**, and **beware** and ask students to write them on the lines. Afterward, meet individually with students. Ask them to read each word on the assessment page. Discuss their results. Use their responses to plan further instruction and review.

Model the Skill

◆ Hand out the Day 1 activity page. Write **chair** on the board and ask students to say the word. Point out that **chair** has one closed syllable. Have students circle **air**. **Say:** *The letters **air** at the end of **chair** sound like **air**. The vowel sound is neither long nor short. When the letter **r** follows a vowel, or vowels, it affects, or controls, the sound that the vowel stands for. These syllables are called **r**-controlled.*

◆ Write **airfare** on the board. **Say:** *I will circle the vowels **ai** and **a**. When words with **r**-controlled vowels are divided into syllables, the vowels and the **r** usually stay in the same syllable. I'll divide the word between the **r** and **f**: **airfare**.*

◆ **Say:** *Now I want to read this word. Both syllables are closed and **r**-controlled. We just learned how to read **air** words so we know what the first syllable sounds like. The second syllable is also closed and **r**-controlled. **Are** is another way to make the **air** sound.* Model reading the two parts of the word and blending them together: **/âr/ /fâr/, airfare**.

◆ Repeat with **ear** as in **bearskin**.

> r-Controlled âr
> Syllables
>
> chair
> air/fare
> bear/skin

r-Controlled /âr/ Syllables

**Divide the following words into syllables where applicable.
Then circle the *r*-controlled sound in each word, as in *fair*.**

chair

_____

airfare

_____

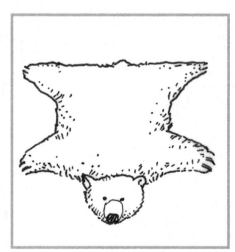

bearskin

_____

Words Divided

Look at the following words. Divide each word into syllables using closed, open, and r-controlled /âr/ syllables. Then read the words to a partner.

List 1:	List 2:	List 3:
hairy	wearing	beware
despair	swimwear	prepare

Choose three words to use in sentences.

1. _____

_____

2. _____

_____

3. _____

_____

r-Controlled /âr/ Syllable Sort

Sort the following words into groups using the *r-controlled /âr/* syllable pattern: *air, ear,* and *are.* Share your results with a partner.

Word List:

impair	tear	pear	compare
fanfare	midair	mare	dairy

air	ear	are

An Irish Outing

Read the letter. Locate the six *r*-controlled /âr/ syllable words and write them at the bottom of the page. Read each word to a partner.

June 25, 2009

Dear Mom,

I'm having a great time in Cork County, Ireland. This morning, I met my friend, Terry Kelly, for breakfast in a city called Derry. Funny name. Sounds like we should be milking Grandpa's cows. Anyway, Terry said I needed to see a real Irish fair, so we walked from the restaurant down to the city square. Wow! Irish folk know how to throw a party. I've never seen so many people having so much fun before lunch.

People were eating, playing carnival games, and listening to live music. For about fifteen minutes we watched some kids play a balloon game. They were completely unaware of us. Finally, one of the boys won a teddy bear. It was cute, but even cuter still was what happened next. He gave the stuffed toy to one of the girls, and she threw it back at him. Kids are the same all over.

Later on, we ate pears, cheese, and bread. Who would have thought that combination would taste so good?

It was a grand affair. Did you catch that? Fair in affair—I'm so funny.

Love you,
Cindy

1. _____   4. _____

2. _____   5. _____

3. _____   6. _____

Assessment

Divide the following words into syllables.

repair	staircase	tearing
bearskin	declare	nightmare

Listen to your teacher say each word. Write the words on the lines.

1. _____

2. _____

3. _____

Overview Vowel Diphthong /oi/ Syllable Pattern

Directions and Sample Answers for Activity Pages

Day 1	See "Model the Skill" below.
Day 2	Read the title and directions aloud. Invite students to divide each word into syllables using open, closed, and vowel diphthong **/oi/** syllable patterns. (**re/coil, sir/loin, ap/point, an/noy, en/joy, em/ploy**) Have students read each word and choose three words to use in sentences.
Day 3	Read the title and directions aloud. Invite students to sort words into groups using the vowel diphthong **/oi/** syllable patterns: (**oi: turmoil, tinfoil, pinpoint, disappoint; oy: overjoy, killjoy, ploy, soy**) Have students read each word and write definitions for three unfamiliar words.
Day 4	Read the title and directions aloud. Invite students to use a dictionary to define the vowel diphthong **/oi/** syllable words. Have students match them to the correct description and then locate the words in the word search. (**ahoy, purloin, corduroy, coy, joint, turquoise**)
Day 5	Read the directions aloud. Allow time for students to complete the first task. (**view/point, boil/ing, tur/quoise, an/noy, kill/joy, a/hoy**) Next, pronounce the words **rejoin** and **destroy** and ask students to write them on the lines. Afterward, meet individually with students. Ask them to read each word on the assessment page. Discuss their results. Use their responses to plan further instruction and review.

Model the Skill

/oi/
Syllables

join
re/join
de/stroy

◆ Hand out the Day 1 activity page. Write **join** on the board and ask students to say the word. Point out that **join** has one closed syllable. Have students circle **oi**. **Say:** *The letters **oi** in the middle of **join** sound like **coin**. The vowel sound is neither long nor short. You can use what you know about letter patterns and syllables to read longer words.*

◆ Write **rejoin** on the board. **Say:** *I will circle the vowels **e** and **oi**. Since **join** is a word and a syllable, I'll divide the word between the **e** and **j**: **re/join**. Copy what I did on your paper.*

◆ **Say:** *Now I want to read this word. The first syllable is open. It probably makes the long **e** sound, so I'll try that vowel sound first. We just learned how to read **join** so we know what the second syllable sounds like. Model reading the two parts of the word and blending them together:* **/re/ /join/, rejoin**.

◆ Point out that **oy** can make the same sound as **oi**, as in **destroy**.

/oi/ Syllables

**Divide the following words into syllables where applicable.
Then circle the /oi/ sound in each word, as in *toy*.**

join

_____

rejoin

_____

destroy

_____

Words Divided

Look at the following words. Divide each word into syllables using closed, open, and vowel diphthong *oi* syllables. Then read the words to a partner.

List 1:	List 2:
recoil	annoy
sirloin	enjoy
appoint	employ

Choose three words to use in sentences.

1. _____

   _____

2. _____

   _____

3. _____

   _____

Vowel Diphthong /oi/ Syllable Sort

Sort the following words into groups using the vowel diphthong
/oi/ syllable pattern: *oi* and *oy*. Share your results with a partner.

Word List

overjoy	pinpoint	turmoil	disappoint
tinfoil	ploy	killjoy	soy

oi	oy

Use a dictionary to define three words that you do not know.
Write the definitions on the lines below.

1. _____

_____

2. _____

_____

3. _____

_____

Word Search

Use a dictionary to define these vowel diphthong /oi/ words and match the words to their descriptions. Then find the words in the word search.

1. something that might be said on a ship:

_____

2. steal: _____

3. a type of cloth: _____

4. shy: _____

5. a place where two things are joined or united: _____

6. a mineral often used in jewelry:

_____

coy

purloin

joint

ahoy

turquoise

corduroy

c	e	s	i	o	u	q	r	u	t
r	j	z	c	s	t	b	m	a	d
n	y	o	d	n	p	u	r	h	q
a	d	t	i	c	u	e	y	o	u
m	c	o	r	d	u	r	o	y	v
f	j	w	k	h	t	i	c	l	g
x	t	p	u	r	l	o	i	n	o

Name _____

Assessment

Divide the following words into syllables.

| viewpoint | boiling | turquoise | annoy | killjoy | ahoy |

Listen to your teacher say each word. Write the words on the lines.

1. _____

2. _____

Overview Vowel Diphthong /ou/ Syllable Pattern

Directions and Sample Answers for Activity Pages

Day 1	See "Model the Skill" below.
Day 2	Read the title and directions aloud. Invite students to divide each word into syllables using open, closed, and vowel diphthong **/ou/** syllable patterns. (**de/vour, an/nounce, pro/found, sur/round, re/nown, down/town, me/ow, al/low**) Have students read each word and choose three words to use in sentences.
Day 3	Read the title and directions aloud. Invite students to sort words into groups using the vowel diphthong **/ou/** syllable patterns: **ou**, **ow**, and both (**ou: recount, playground, devout; ow: kowtow, anyhow, ballgown; both: powerhouse, chowhound**) Have students choose three unknown words and define them using a dictionary.
Day 4	Read the title and directions aloud. Invite students to cut and glue the sentence parts together to form sentences. (I asked for a dog at Christmas, and my parents bought me a greyhound. Girls are not allowed in our clubhouse. The campground has cabins and tent space. Somehow there is a way to surprise my mother for her birthday. My dad is not at home because he went to the gym for a workout. We saw a real powwow at the Native American reservation.)
Day 5	Read the directions aloud. Allow time for students to complete the first task. (**a/mount, ac/count, de/vour, bow/wow, eye/brow, Mos/cow**) Next, pronounce the words **recount** and **powwow** and ask students to write them on the lines. Afterward, meet individually with students. Ask them to read each word on the assessment page. Discuss their results. Use their responses to plan further instruction and review.

Model the Skill

◆ Hand out the Day 1 activity page. Write **house** on the board and ask students to say the word. Point out that **house** has one closed syllable. Have students circle **ou**. **Say:** *The letters **ou** in the middle of **house** sound like **round**, and the final **e** is silent. The vowel sound is neither long nor short.*

◆ Write **lighthouse** on the board. **Say:** *I will circle the vowels **i** and **ou**. We see four consonants between the vowels, but the **gh** is a part of long **i** digraph **igh**. I can't divide a vowel digraph, so I'll divide the word between the **t** and **h**: **light/house**.*

◆ **Say:** *Now I want to read this word. The first syllable is closed, but it has an **igh** in it. I know **igh** makes the long **i** sound, so I'll try that sound first. The second syllable is also closed and has an **ou** in it. That syllable should make a sound like **mouse**.* Model reading the two parts of the word and blending them together: **/līt/ /hous/**, **lighthouse**. Repeat with **ow** as in **tower**. (**tow/er**)

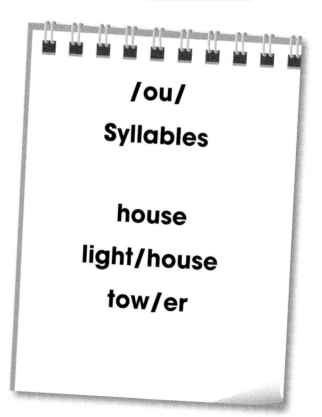

/ou/
Syllables

house
light/house
tow/er

/ou/ Syllables

**Divide the following words into syllables where applicable.
Then circle the /ou/ sound in each word, as in cow.**

house

_____

lighthouse

_____

tower

_____

Words Divided

Look at the following words. Divide each word into syllables using closed, open, and vowel diphthong /ou/ syllables. Then read the words to a partner.

List 1:	List 2:
devour	renown
announce	downtown
profound	meow
surround	allow

Choose three words to use in sentences.

1. _____

   _____

2. _____

   _____

3. _____

   _____

Vowel Diphthong /ou/ Syllable Sort

Sort the following words into groups using the vowel diphthong /ou/ syllable pattern: *ou* and *ow*. Share your results with a partner.

Word List

kowtow	devout	chowhound	recount
powerhouse	playground	anyhow	ballgown

ou	ow	both

Use a dictionary to define three words that you do not know. Write the definitions on the lines below.

1. _____

_____

2. _____

_____

3. _____

_____

Sentence Scramble

Cut out the sentence parts and then put the parts together to form sentences that make sense. Glue correctly formed sentences onto a piece of notebook paper. Read the sentences to a partner.

I asked for a dog at Christmas, and	he went to the gym for a workout.
Girls are not allowed	at the Native American reservation.
The campground has	surprise my mother for her birthday.
Somehow there is a way to	my parents bought me a greyhound.
My dad is not at home because	cabins and tent space.
We saw a real powwow	in our clubhouse.

Name _____

Assessment

Divide the following words into syllables.

amount	account	devour	bowwow	eyebrow	Moscow

Listen to your teacher say each word. Write the words on the lines.

1. _____

2. _____

Overview Vowel Diphthong /oo/ Syllable Pattern

Directions and Sample Answers for Activity Pages

Day 1	See "Model the Skill" below.
Day 2	Read the title and directions aloud. Invite students to divide each word into syllables using open, closed, and vowel diphthong **/oo/** syllable patterns. (**heir/loom, mon/soon, group/ing, croup/y, cur/few, re/view, con/strue, sub/due**) Have students read each word and choose three words to use in sentences.
Day 3	Read the title and directions aloud. Invite students to sort words into groups using the vowel diphthong **/oo/** syllable patterns: **oo, ou, ew,** and **ue** (oo: **pontoon, lampoon;** ou: **soup, in-group;** ew: **interview, anew;** ue: **miscue, residue**) Have students choose three unknown words and define them using a dictionary.
Day 4	Read the title and directions aloud. Invite students to locate the words in the word search and then match each word to the correct sentence. (1. **soup**, 2. **overdue**, 3. **chew**, 4. **raccoon**, 5. **bassoon**, 6. **avenue**, 7. **pew**, 8. **group**)
Day 5	Read the directions aloud. Allow time for students to complete the first task. (**har/poon, group/ing, out/grew/, with/drew, pur/sue, un/true**) Next, pronounce the words **cartoon, regroup, anew,** and **miscue** and ask students to write them on the lines. Afterward, meet individually with students. Ask them to read each word on the assessment page. Discuss their results. Use their responses to plan further instruction and review.

Model the Skill

/oo/ Syllables

moon

car/toon

re/group

ca/shew

pur/sue

◆ Hand out the Day 1 activity. Write **moon** on the board and ask students to say the word. Point out that **moon** has one closed syllable. Have students circle **oo. Say:** *The letters **oo** in the middle of **moon** sound like **soon**. The vowel sound is neither long nor short. You can use what you know about letter patterns and syllables to read longer words.*

◆ Write **cartoon** on the board. **Say:** *I will circle the vowels **a** and **oo**. There are two consonants between the vowels, so I'll divide the word between the **r** and **t**: **car/toon**. Copy what I did on your paper.*

◆ **Say:** *Now I want to read this word. The first syllable is closed, and it has an **r**-controlled **a** in it. That should sound like **are**. The second syllable is also closed and has an **oo** in it. This syllable should make the sound like **moon** and **soon**.* Model reading the two parts of the word and blending them together: **/cär/ toon/.**

◆ Repeat with **ou, ew,** and **ue** as in **regroup, cashew,** and **pursue.**

/oo/ Syllables

Divide the following words into syllables where applicable.
Then circle the /oo/ sound in each word, as in *soon*.

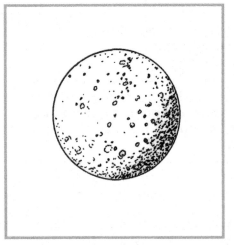

moon

_____

cartoon

_____

regroup

_____

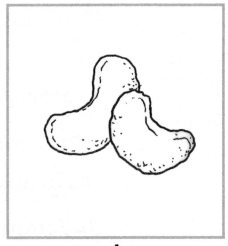

cashew

_____

pursue

_____

Words Divided

Look at the following words. Divide each word into syllables using closed, open, and vowel diphthong /oo/ syllables. Then read the words to a partner.

List 1:	List 2:	List 3:	List 4:
heirloom	grouping	curfew	construe
monsoon	croupy	review	subdue

Choose three words to use in sentences.

1. _____

_____

2. _____

_____

3. _____

_____

Vowel Diphthong /oo/ Syllable Sort

Sort the following words into groups using the vowel diphthong /oo/ syllable pattern: *oo, ou, ew,* and *ue*. Share your results with a partner.

Word List

interview	pontoon	lampoon	soup
residue	in-group	miscue	anew

oo	ou	ew	ue

Use a dictionary to define three words that you do not know.
Write the definitions on the lines below.

1. _____

   _____

2. _____

   _____

3. _____

   _____

Word Search

Locate the words in the word search and then match each word to the correct sentence.

raccoon	soup	chew	overdue
bassoon	group	pew	avenue

g	r	o	u	p	a	o
e	g	w	b	c	h	v
u	o	n	e	l	m	e
n	o	o	c	c	a	r
e	n	o	j	q	u	d
v	w	s	v	s	x	u
a	e	s	o	u	p	e
z	h	a	v	y	e	a
t	c	b	p	w	w	k

We had chicken _____ for supper.

My library books are _____. I'm going to have a big fee.

It's not nice to _____ your food with your mouth open.

A _____ turned over our garbage cans last night.

My sister plays the _____ in the high school band.

I want to walk down Fifth _____.

At the meeting, my parents sat in the last _____.

I was in the last _____, so I didn't board the bus until almost 8:30.

Assessment

Divide the following words into syllables.

harpoon	**outgrew**	**pursue**
grouping	**withdrew**	**untrue**

Listen to your teacher say each word. Write the words on the lines.

1. _____

2. _____

3. _____

4. _____

Overview Vowel Diphthong /o͝o/ Syllable Pattern

Directions and Sample Answers for Activity Pages

Day 1	See "Model the Skill" below.
Day 2	Read the title and directions aloud. Invite students to divide each word into syllables using open, closed, and vowel diphthong /o͝o/ syllable patterns. (**red/wood, drift/wood, a/foot, mis/took, am/bush, rose/bush, pul/ley**) Have students read each word and choose three words to use in sentences.
Day 3	Read the title and directions aloud. Invite students to sort words into groups using the vowel diphthong /o͝o/ syllable patterns: **oo** and **u**. (**oo: woolen, overlook, underfoot, childhood; u: bulletin, push-pull, pit bull, fullest**) Have students choose two unknown words and define them using a dictionary.
Day 4	Read the title and directions aloud. Invite students to draw a line between the words in the box to make two- or three-syllable words. Then ask students to choose those words from the list to fill in the blanks. (1. **Sitting Bull**, 2. **rosebush**, 3. **neighborhood**, 4. **chock-full**, 5. **Robin Hood**, 6. **notebook**)
Day 5	Read the directions aloud. Allow time for students to complete the first task. (**book/case, un/hook, am/bush, push/y**) Next, pronounce the words **afoot** and **bully** and ask students to write them on the lines. Afterward, meet individually with students. Ask them to read each word on the assessment page. Discuss their results. Use their responses to plan further instruction and review.

Model the Skill

◆ Hand out the Day 1 activity page. Write **cook** on the board and ask students to say the word. Point out that **cook** has one closed syllable. Have students circle **oo**. **Say:** *The letters **oo** in the middle of **cook** sound like **hook**. The vowel sound is neither long nor short. You can use what you know about letter patterns and syllables to read longer words.*

◆ Write **bookmark** on the board. **Say:** *I will circle the vowels **oo** and **a**. There are two consonants between the vowels, so I'll divide the word between the **k** and **m**: **book/mark**. Copy what I did on your paper.*

◆ **Say:** *Now I want to read this word. The first syllable is closed, and it has an **oo** in it like **hook**. The second syllable is also closed and it has an **r**-controlled **a** in it that sounds like **are**. Model reading the two parts of the word and blending them together: /bo͝ok/ /märk/.*

◆ Repeat with **bully**. (**bul/ly**) Have students circle the **u**. Point out that **u** can make the same sound as **oo** as in **book**. Identify syllables as open or closed.

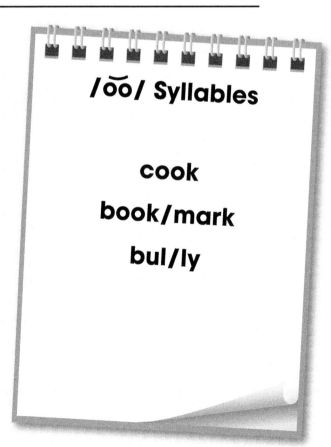

/o͝o/ Syllables

cook

book/mark

bul/ly

/ŏŏ/ Syllables

**Divide the following words into syllables where applicable.
Then circle the /ŏŏ/ sound in each word, as in *look*.**

cook

_____

bookmark

_____

bully

_____

Words Divided

Look at the following words. Divide each word into syllables using closed, open, and vowel diphthong /o͝o/ syllables. Then read the words to a partner.

List 1:	List 2:
redwood	ambush
driftwood	rosebush
afoot	pulley
mistook	

Choose three words to use in sentences.

1. _____

_____

2. _____

_____

3. _____

_____

Vowel Diphthong /o͝o/ Syllable Sort

Sort the following words into groups using the vowel diphthong /o͝o/
syllable pattern: *oo* and *u*. Share your results with a partner.

Word List

bulletin	push-pull	childhood	pit bull
underfoot	woolen	fullest	overlook

oo	u

Use a dictionary to define two words that you do not know.
Write the definitions on the lines below.

1. _____

   _____

2. _____

   _____

Make Words

Draw a line between the words in the box to make two- or three-syllable words. Then choose those words from the box to fill in the blanks.

Sitting	bush
note	full
rose	Hood
neighbor	book
Robin	hood
chock-	Bull

We learned about _____ at the Native American museum.

My best friend's _____ won the Garden Club's contest.

Our _____ has a playground, swimming pool, and tennis courts.

The cookies were _____ of nuts and little chocolate candies.

_____ is a great movie.

I left my _____ on top of the car and lost it.

Assessment

Divide the following words into syllables.

bookcase	**unhook**	**ambush**	**pushy**

Listen to your teacher say each word. Write the words on the lines.

1. _____

2. _____

Overview Vowel Diphthong /ô/ Syllable Pattern

Directions and Sample Answers for Activity Pages

Day 1	See "Model the Skill" below.
Day 2	Read the title and directions aloud. Invite students to divide each word into syllables using open, closed, and vowel diphthong **/ô/** syllable patterns. (**bean/stalk, ap/pall, de/fault, dis/traught, out/law, jig/saw, bos/sy, strong/ly**) Have students read each word and choose three words to use in sentences.
Day 3	Read the title and directions aloud. Invite students to sort words into groups using the vowel diphthong **/ô/** syllable patterns: **a, au, aw,** and **o**. (**a: asphalt, install; au: saunter, assault; aw: prawn, withdraw; o: across, froth**) Have students choose two unknown words and define them using a dictionary.
Day 4	Read the title and directions aloud. Invite students to locate the ten vowel diphthong **/ô/** syllable words in the letter. Read each word to a partner. (**Cross, oblong, straw, haunted, squall, off, brought, rainfall, brawny, caught**)
Day 5	Read the directions aloud. Allow time for students to complete the first task. (**re/call, haunt/ed, out/law, bos/sy**) Next, pronounce the words **install**, **fault**, **jigsaw**, and **frosty** and ask students to write them on the lines. Afterward, meet individually with students. Ask them to read each word on the assessment page. Discuss their results. Use their responses to plan further instruction and review.

Model the Skill

◆ Hand out the Day 1 activity page. Write **ball** on the board and ask students to say the word. Point out that **ball** has one closed syllable. Have students circle **a** on their activity sheets. **Say:** *The letter **a** in the middle of **ball** sounds like **wall**. The vowel sound is neither long nor short. You can use what you know about letter patterns and syllables to read longer words.*

◆ Write **recall** on the board. **Say:** *I will circle the vowels **e** and **a**. There is one consonant between the vowels, so I'll divide the word before the **c**: **re/call**. Copy what I did on your paper.*

◆ **Say:** *Now I want to read this word. The first syllable is open so it probably makes the long **e** sound. I'll try that first. The second syllable is closed and has an **a** in it like **ball**.* Model reading the two parts of the word and blending them together: **/rē/ /kôl/**.

◆ Repeat with **faulty**, **seesaw**, and **frosty**. (**fault/y, see/saw, frost/y**) Have students circle the **au** in **faulty**, the **aw** in **seesaw**, and the **o** in **frosty**. Point out that **au, aw,** and **o** can make the same sound as the **a** in **call**.

/ô/ Syllables

ball

re/call

fault/y

see/saw

frost/y

/ô/ Syllables

Divide the following words into syllables where applicable.
Then circle the /ô/ sound in each word, as in *tall*.

ball

_____

recall

_____

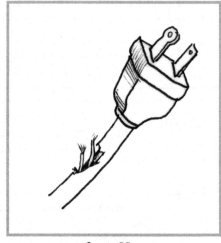

faulty

_____

seesaw

_____

frosty

_____

Words Divided

Look at the following words. Divide each word into syllables using closed, open, and vowel diphthong /ô/ syllables. Then read the words to a partner.

List 1:	List 2:	List 3:	List 4:
beanstalk	default	outlaw	bossy
appall	distraught	jigsaw	strongly

Choose three words to use in sentences.

1. _____

_____

2. _____

_____

3. _____

_____

Vowel Diphthong /ô/ Syllable Sort

Sort the following words into groups using the vowel diphthong /ô/
syllable pattern: *a, au, aw,* and *o*. Share your results with a partner.

Word List

| withdraw | asphalt | froth | saunter |
| across | assault | install | prawn |

a	au	aw	o

Use a dictionary to define two words that you do not know.
Write the definitions on the lines below.

1. _____

_____

2. _____

_____

An English Vacation

Read the letter. Locate the ten vowel diphthong /ô/ syllable words and write them at the bottom of the page. Read each word to a partner.

July 18, 2009

Dear Aunt Jane,

I'm having a wonderful time on my English vacation. I'm staying at a farm that was used by the Red Cross during World War II. The farmhouse is in an oblong shape and has a straw thatched roof. An old man in the village says that this house is haunted, but I haven't seen any ghost yet.

A squall came in off the English Channel the other day and brought five inches of rainfall. You should have seen the brawny men down at the docks. They caught so many fish that they didn't know what to do. Where were they going to put so many fish? I think they packed many of them in ice.

I'll write again in a few days. I'm visiting a castle on Saturday. Can't wait.

Your nephew,
James

1. _____   6. _____

2. _____   7. _____

3. _____   8. _____

4. _____   9. _____

5. _____   10. _____

Assessment

Divide the following words into syllables.

recall	haunted	outlaw	bossy

Listen to your teacher say each word. Write the words on the lines.

1. _____

2. _____

3. _____

4. _____

Overview Consonant + le, al, el Words

Directions and Sample Answers for Activity Pages

Day 1	See "Model the Skill" below.
Day 2	Read the title and directions aloud. Invite students to divide each word into syllables using open and closed syllable patterns. (**sad/dle, twin/kle, bee/tle, bru/tal, den/tal, fo/cal, la/bel, duf/fel, stru/del**) Have students read each word and choose three words to use in sentences.
Day 3	Read the title and directions aloud. Invite students to sort the words into the three word groups: consonant + **le**, consonant + **al**, and consonant + **el**. (**le: simple, circle, grapple; al: rental, journal, vocal; el: mussel, shrivel, model**) Have students choose two unknown words and define them using a dictionary.
Day 4	Read the title and directions aloud. Invite students to use the consonant + **le, al**, and **el** endings to finish the words. (**marble, pickle, medal, global, chisel, rebel**) Then have students choose three words and write them in sentences on the lines provided.
Day 5	Read the directions aloud. Allow time for students to complete the first task. (**sim/ple, den/tal, mus/sel**) Next, pronounce the words **saddle, vocal,** and **label** and ask students to write them on the lines. Afterward, meet individually with students. Ask them to read each word on the assessment page. Discuss their results. Use their responses to plan further instruction and review.

Model the Skill

◆ Hand out the Day 1 activity page. Write **table, cymbal,** and **kernel** on the board. Have students circle the **le, al,** and **el** on their activity pages. **Say:** *Words that end in -le, -al,* and *-el all stand for the same sound, /+ l/ (pronounced /ul/). These letter pairs and the consonant that comes before them usually form the last syllable in a word.*

◆ **Say:** *Look at* **table***. I know that* **ble** *forms the last syllable. So the first syllable must be* **ta***. (**ta/ble***) Copy what I did on your paper.*

◆ **Say:** *Now I want to read* **table***. The first syllable is open so it should have a long* **a** *sound. I'll try that first. The second syllable makes the /bul/ sound.* Model reading the two parts of the word and blending them together: **/tā/ /bul/**.

◆ Repeat with **cymbal** and **kernel**. (**cym/bal, ker/nel**) Identify syllables as open or closed. Model reading the two words: **/sim/ /bul/** and **/kûr/ /nul/**.

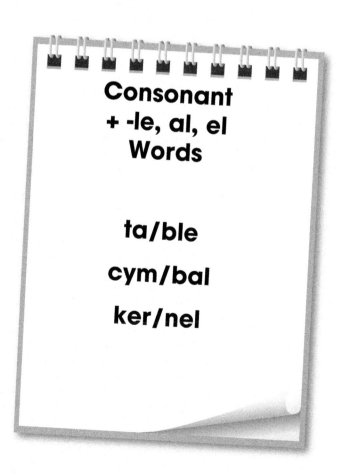

Consonant + -le, al, el Words

ta/ble

cym/bal

ker/nel

-le, -al, -el Words

Divide the following words into syllables. Then circle the *-le, -al,* or *-el* endings.

table

_____

cymbal

_____

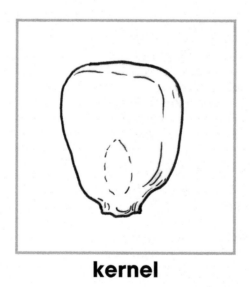

kernel

_____

Words Divided

Look at the following words. Divide each consonant + *le, al,* and *el* word into syllables using open and closed syllables. Then read the words to a partner.

List 1:	List 2:	List 3:
saddle	brutal	label
twinkle	dental	duffel
beetle	focal	strudel

Choose three words to use in sentences.

1. _____

   _____

2. _____

   _____

3. _____

   _____

Name _____

Consonant + le, al, el Word Sort

Sort the following words into groups using consonant + *le, al,* and *el.*
Share your results with a partner.

Word List

journal	mussel	vocal
model	circle	shrivel
simple	rental	grapple

le	al	el

Use a dictionary to define two words that you do not know.
Write the definitions on the lines below.

1. _____

_____

2. _____

_____

Add the Ending

Use the consonant + *le, al,* and *el* endings to finish the words.

dal	bel	kle	ble	sel	bal

mar_____   glo_____

pic_____   chi_____

me_____   re_____

Choose three words and write them in sentences on the lines provided.

1. _____

_____

2. _____

_____

3. _____

_____

Name _____

Assessment

Divide the following words into syllables.

simple	dental	mussel

Listen to your teacher say each word. Write the words on the lines.

1. _____

2. _____

3. _____

Overview Compound Words

Directions and Sample Answers for Activity Pages

Day 1	See "Model the Skill" below.
Day 2	Read the title and directions aloud. Invite students to sort words into the three compound word groups: open, closed, and hyphenated. (open: **hand puppet, fire station, fire engine**; closed: **handshake, handmade, fireworks, firefly, playground, playpen, playhouse**; hyphenated: **hands-on, hand-feed, fire-eater, play-offs**) Have students read each word. (Students could sort these words by compound families: hand, fire, play.)
Day 3	Read the title and directions aloud. Invite students to draw literal interpretations of each compound word. Have students read the words, define them, and use them in sentences.
Day 4	Read the title and directions aloud. Invite students to answer the riddles and complete the clozed sentences using words from the compound word list. (**sea horses, watchdog, hot dog, two-tired, backboard, sunburn, air mattress, step-by-step**)
Day 5	Read the directions aloud. Allow time for students to complete the first task. (**step-by-step, sea horse, sunburn, merry-go-round, air mattress, watchdog**) Next, pronounce the words **horsefly, light-headed**, and **bed rest** and ask students to write them on the lines. Afterward, meet individually with students. Ask them to read each word on the assessment page. Discuss their results. Use their responses to plan further instruction and review.

Model the Skill

◆ Hand out the Day 1 activity page. Write **fire drill**, **doghouse**, and **merry-go-round** on the board and read them aloud.

◆ **Say:** *These words are all compound words. We have three types of compound words. Open compound words like **fire drill** are made up of two separate words. Closed compound words like **doghouse** are made up of combined words. Hyphenated compound words like **merry-go-round** are made up of two or more words separated by a hyphen or hyphens.*

◆ Tell students that identifying compound words is easy. When a compound word is divided, each small word must mean something on its own. For example, **doghouse** is made up of two small words: **dog** and **house**. Explain that sometimes knowing the meanings of the smaller words helps you to define a compound word, but not always (**butterfly, hot dog**).

◆ Help students identify the small words that make up **fire drill**, **merry-go-round**, and **doorknob**. Then ask students to complete the sentences at the bottom of the activity page.

Compound Words

open:

fire drill

closed:

doghouse
doorknob

hyphenated:
merry-go-round

Compound Word Types

Divide the following words into syllables. Then complete the sentences below.

fire drill

_____

doghouse

_____

merry-go-round

_____

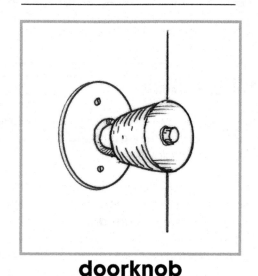

doorknob

_____

_____ is made up of the words _____ and _____.

_____ is made up of the words _____ and _____.

_____ is made up of the words _____, _____, and
_____.

_____ is made up of the words _____ and _____.

Name _____

Compound Word Sort

Read the following words. Sort them by the three compound word types: open, closed, and hyphenated. Share your results with a partner.

Word List

hands-on	handmade	fireworks	firefly
fire station	fire-eater	fire engine	playground
hand puppet	hand-feed	playpen	
playhouse	play-offs	handshake	

Open	Closed	Hyphenated

What is another way to sort these words?

Name _____

Can a Horse Fly?

Many compound words do not mean what their smaller words mean. Read the compound words below. Draw the literal meaning of each word. Ask yourself: How does a bed rest? How does a horse fly? What might *light-headed* look like?

Word List

bed rest	horsefly	light-headed

Identify the meaning of each word by using a dictionary.
Use each word in a sentence.

1. _____

_____

2. _____

_____

3. _____

_____

Using Your Brain

Read the riddles below. Use words from the compound word list to answer the riddles.

What horses are the best swimmers?

_____

What kind of dog gets the most ticks?

_____

What kind of dog likes living where it's sunny and warm?

_____

Why do bicycles fall over?

_____

Read the sentences below. Use words from the compound word list to fill in the blanks.

Without the _____, a basketball would end up in the stands.

Ouch! I was out in the sun too long and got a _____.

When I go camping, I sleep on an _____.

There are _____ instructions to tell me how to put this thing together.

Compound Word List

two-tired	backboard	sunburn	sea horses
hot dog	watchdog	step-by-step	air mattress

Assessment

The following compound words are written incorrectly.
Write them correctly in the space provided.

1. stepbystep   _____

2. seahorse   _____

3. sun-burn   _____

4. merrygoround   _____

5. airmattress   _____

6. watch-dog   _____

Listen to your teacher say each word. Write the words on the lines.

1. _____

2. _____

3. _____

Overview Silent Letter Words

Directions and Sample Answers for Activity Pages

Day 1	See "Model the Skill" below.
Day 2	Read the title and directions aloud. Invite students to divide each silent letter word into syllables using open and closed syllable patterns. (**wrig/gle, wres/tle, knap/sack, knowl/edge, as/sign, re/sign, rhu/barb, rhyth/mic**) Have students read each word and choose three words to use in sentences.
Day 3	Read the title and directions aloud. Invite students to sort words into silent letter word groups: **wr, kn, gn,** and **rh**. (**wr: wrinkle, wreck; kn: knotty, knight; gn**: **gnome, gnat; rh: rhyme, rhea**) Have students choose two unknown words and define them using a dictionary.
Day 4	Read the title and directions aloud. Invite students to unscramble the sentences and write them on the lines. Then have students draw a picture that shows what is happening in each sentence. Have students read each sentence to a partner. (I hung a wreath on the front door. I scraped my knuckle on the rock. I found a gneiss rock in the creek. Rhinestones sparkle when light hits them.)
Day 5	Read the directions aloud. Allow time for students to complete the first task. (**wrig/gle, knap/sack, re/sign, rhi/no**) Next, pronounce the words **wrinkle, knotty, design,** and **rhea** and ask students to write them on the lines. Afterward, meet individually with students. Ask them to read each word on the assessment page. Discuss their results. Use their responses to plan further instruction and review.

Model the Skill

◆ Hand out the Day 1 activity page. Write the word **wrap** on the board and circle the **w**. **Say:** *Certain words have silent letters. In this word, the letter **w** is silent when it appears before **r**. You can use what you know about silent letters to read longer words.*

◆ Write **wrapping** on the board. **Say:** *I will circle the **a** and **i**. I know double letter words are divided between the letters, so I'll divide this word between the double **p**. (**wrap/ping**)*

◆ **Say:** *Now I want to read **wrapping**. The first syllable is closed, so it should make the short **a** sound. I'll try that first. I also know that the **w** is silent when it appears before **r**, so I won't make the /w/ sound. I'll begin the word with the /r/ sound. The second syllable is also closed. It makes the same sound as in **sing**. Model reading the two parts of the word and blending them together: /rap/ /ping/.*

◆ Repeat with **knickers, design,** and **rhino**. Explain that **k** and **g** are silent before **n**, and **h** is silent following **r**. Identify syllables as open or closed. Model reading the words. (/nik/ /ûrs/, /di/ /zīn/, and /rī/ /nō/)

Silent Letters

wrap/ping

knick/ers

de/sign

rhi/no

Silent Letters

Divide the following words into syllables where applicable.
Then circle the silent letter in each word.

wrap

wrapping

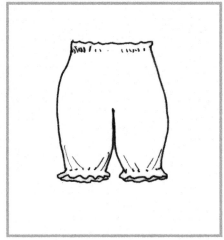
knickers

_____ _____ _____

design

rhino

_____ _____

Name _____

Words Divided

Look at the following words. Divide each silent letter word into syllables using open and closed syllables. Then read the words to a partner.

List 1:	List 2:	List 3:	List 4:
wriggle	knapsack	assign	rhubarb
wrestle	knowledge	resign	rhythmic

Choose three words to use in sentences.

1. _____

_____

2. _____

_____

3. _____

_____

Silent Letter Word Sort

Sort the following silent letter words into groups. Share your results with a partner.

Word List

gnome	**knotty**	**knight**	**rhea**
wrinkle	**rhyme**	**wreck**	**gnat**

wr	**kn**	**gn**	**rh**

**Use a dictionary to define two words that you do not know.
Write the definitions on the lines below.**

1. _____

   _____

2. _____

   _____

Sentence Scramble

Unscramble the sentences and write them on the lines. Then draw a picture that shows what is happening in each sentence. Read your sentences to a partner.

the hung I wreath on door a front

_____

_____

rock knuckle scraped my I the on

_____

_____

creek found I rock gneiss the a in

_____

_____

sparkle hits rhinestones light when them

_____

_____

Assessment

Divide the following words into syllables.

wriggle	**knapsack**	**resign**	**rhino**

Listen to your teacher say each word. Write the words on the lines.

1. _____

2. _____

3. _____

4. _____

Overview Contractions

Directions and Sample Answers for Activity Pages

Day 1	See "Model the Skill" below.
Day 2	Read the title and directions aloud. Invite students to draw a line from the word pairs to the contractions. (**have not/haven't, do not/don't, we have/we've, you are/you're, is not/isn't, she will/she'll, I will/I'll, should not/shouldn't, I have/I've, he would/he'd**) Have students read each contraction and choose three contractions to use in sentences.
Day 3	Read the title and directions aloud. Invite students to read the sentences and locate the contractions. Have students insert apostrophes in the appropriate places. (**aren't, I'll, didn't, shouldn't, I'm, can't, don't, We'd, They're, We'll**)
Day 4	Read the title and directions aloud. Invite students to locate the fourteen contractions in the letter. Have students read each word to a partner. (**We're, didn't, He'll, I'd, don't, won't, should've, couldn't, we'd, You're, We'd, Let's, We'll, we've**)
Day 5	Read the directions aloud. Allow time for students to complete the first task. (**they're, we're, won't, shouldn't, she'd**) Next, pronounce the words **aren't, isn't, we'd**, and **we've** and ask students to write them on the lines. Afterward, meet individually with students. Ask them to read each word on the assessment page. Discuss their results. Use their responses to plan further instruction and review.

Model the Skill

◆ Hand out the Day 1 activity page. Write the words **are not** and **aren't** on the board. **Say:** *A contraction is a short form of two words. One or more letters is replaced by an apostrophe. Notice how I made **are not** into **aren't**. I removed the **o** and replaced it with an apostrophe. You can make contractions out of many words.*

◆ Write the following sentence on the board: *He is going outside because it is hot.* **Say:** *I can make **He is** and **it is** into contractions.* Write **He's** and **it's** under the respective words. **Say:** *In both cases, I removed **i** in **is** and replaced it with an apostrophe. Copy what I did on your paper.*

◆ Repeat with **did not, I have**, and **we will**. (**didn't, I've**, and **we'll**) Write a sentence for each pair of words and then rewrite word pairs into contractions.

◆ Repeat with **he would** and **she would** (**he'd, she'd**), and **will not** (**won't**). Explain that many letters are removed from these contractions.

Contractions

are + not = aren't

he + is = he's

I + have = I've

we + will = we'll

he + would = he'd

she + would = she'd

will + not + won't

Contractions

Write contractions for the following words.

1. are not   _____

2. he is   _____

3. it is   _____

4. did not   _____

5. I have   _____

6. we will   _____

7. he would   _____

8. she would   _____

9. will not   _____

Contraction Action

Look at the following words. Draw a line to match the word pairs to the correct contraction.

have not	shouldn't
do not	she'll
we have	I'll
you are	isn't
is not	we've
she will	he'd
I will	don't
should not	haven't
I have	you're
he would	I've

Choose three contractions to use in sentences.

1. _____

   _____

2. _____

   _____

3. _____

   _____

Where Does the Apostrophe Go?

Read the following sentences. They contain contractions with missing apostrophes. Insert the apostrophe in the correct place.

Tom and Jane arent going to the party.

Ill need my book later.

He didnt look very happy.

Shouldnt you get ready to go to the play?

Im coming home early.

I cant stay out too late because I have camp in the morning.

Dont run down the hallway.

Wed better go before somebody gets in trouble.

Theyre boarding the plane at 10:00 in the morning.

Well have plenty of time to play.

We're Sorry

Read the letter. Locate the fourteen contractions and write them at the bottom of the page. Read each word to a partner.

Dear Mr. and Mrs. Miller,

    We're writing this letter to tell you that we hit our baseball through your window while you were out. We didn't mean to do it. Jake was working on his pop fly balls. He'll need more work with fly balls, I'd have to say. But don't worry. We won't be hitting baseballs your way again.

    We know we should've hit the baseball into the woods. But Jake couldn't stand the thought of hitting the ball over there. He thought we'd never find it again.

    You're the best people in our neighborhood. We'd like to make it up to you. Let's work out a plan. We'll work for you until we've earned the price of fixing your window.

               Sam and Jake

1. _____

2 _____

3. _____

4. _____

5. _____

6. _____

7. _____

8. _____

9. _____

10. _____

11. _____

12. _____

13. _____

14. _____

Assessment

Read the following word pairs. Write their contractions on the lines provided.

they are _____

we are _____

will not _____

should not _____

she would _____

Listen to your teacher say each word. Write the words on the lines.

1. _____

2. _____

3. _____

4. _____

Overview Regular and Irregular Plurals

Directions and Sample Answers for Activity Pages

Day 1	See "Model the Skill" below.
Day 2	Read the title and directions aloud. Invite students to look at the singular nouns and write regular plural words for each noun. Have students read each word to a partner. Then have them choose three words and use them in sentences. (**riddles, actors, fields, churches, taxes, dresses, flurries, bullies, armies**)
Day 3	Read the title and directions aloud. Invite students to look at the singular nouns and write irregular plural words for each noun. Have students read each word to a partner. Then have them choose three words and use them in sentences. (**geese, mice, oxen, knives, wives, calves, deer, dozen, sheep**)
Day 4	Read the title and directions aloud. Invite students to locate eight regular and nine irregular plurals in the narrative. Have students read each word to a partner. (regular: **cows, names, cobras, groups, schools, shoals, coats, lizards**; irregular: **jellyfish, fish, fish, herring, oxen, geese, sheep, deer, mice**)
Day 5	Read the directions aloud. Allow time for students to complete the first task. (**bears, axes, cities, women, leaves, moose**) Next, pronounce the words **riddles, taxes, bullies, geese, wolves,** and **sheep** and ask students to write them on the lines. Afterward, meet individually with students. Ask them to read each word on the assessment page. Discuss their results. Use their responses to plan further instruction and review.

Model the Skill

◆ Hand out the Day 1 activity page. Write the words **cake, dish,** and **baby** on the board. Write the letters **s, z, ch, sh, x** in parentheses next to **dish**.

◆ Say: *Plural* means more than one thing. We have many ways to make plurals. Look at the words on the board. Most nouns are made plural by simply adding an *-s*, as in *cake*. Write **cakes** beside **cake**. Say: Words ending in *sh*, *ch*, *c*, and *x*, like the word *dish*, need an *-es* to make the plural form, like *dishes*. Write **dishes** beside **dish**. Say: For words ending in *y*, drop the *y* and add *-ies*, like *baby—babies*. Write **babies** beside **baby**. Repeat with **dog, fox,** and **berry**. (**dogs, foxes, berries**)

◆ Write the words **child, wolf,** and **fish**. Say: *Some plural words don't follow the* **s, es, ies** *pattern. These plurals are called irregular plurals. Look at* **child**. *It becomes* **children**. Write **children** next to **child**. Say: *Look at* **wolf**. *We drop the* **f** *and add* **-ves**. Write **wolves** next to **wolf**. Say: *Now look at* **fish**. *Some plural words are exactly the same as their singular form. One fish, two fish, not* **fishes**. Write **fish** beside **fish**. Say: *Since irregular plurals do not follow rules, they must be memorized.* Repeat with **man, loaf,** and **moose**. (**men, loaves, moose**)

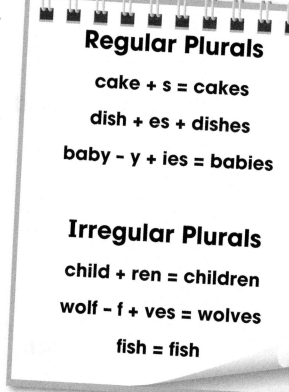

Regular Plurals

cake + s = cakes

dish + es + dishes

baby - y + ies = babies

Irregular Plurals

child + ren = children

wolf - f + ves = wolves

fish = fish

Regular Plurals

 **cake**  _____

 **dish**  _____

 **baby**  _____

1. dog _____   2. fox _____   3. berry _____

Irregular Plurals

child  _____

wolf  _____

fish  _____

1. man _____   2. loaf _____   3. moose _____

Name _____

Follow the Rule

Look at the following singular nouns. For each word, write the regular plural form. Read each plural word to a partner.

List 1:	List 2:	List 3:
riddle _____	church _____	flurry _____
actor _____	tax _____	bully _____
field _____	dress _____	army _____

Choose three words to use in sentences.

1. _____

_____

2. _____

_____

3. _____

_____

Name _____

Remember It!

Look at the following singular nouns. For each word, write the irregular plural form.

List 1:	**List 2:**	**List 3:**
goose _____	knife _____	deer _____
mouse _____	wife _____	dozen _____
ox _____	calf _____	sheep _____

Choose three words to use in sentences.

1. _____

   _____

2. _____

   _____

3. _____

   _____

Unit 21 • Everyday Phonics Intervention Activities Grade 4 • © Newmark Learning, LLC

Animal Groups

Read the narrative on animal groups. Circle the eight regular plural nouns. Underline the nine irregular plural nouns. Write them at the bottom of the page. Read each word to a partner.

You may have heard of a herd of cows. But did you know that almost every animal has a group name?

Some of the names might make you think of the animal, like a quiver of cobras. Some sound plain silly, like a smack of jellyfish.

Groups of fish are called schools. But some fish, like herring, swim in shoals. More than one ox makes a span of oxen. A group of geese is called a gaggle.

You can make many wool coats from a drove of sheep. A few deer make up a herd or a leash. A mouse might join a horde or mischief of mice. Have you ever seen a lounge of lizards?

Regular Plurals	**Irregular Plurals**
1. _____	1. _____
2. _____	2. _____
3. _____	3. _____
4. _____	4. _____
5. _____	5. _____
6. _____	6. _____
7. _____	7. _____
8. _____	8. _____
	9. _____

Assessment

Read the following singular nouns. Write their plurals on the lines provided.

bear   _____

ax   _____

city   _____

woman   _____

leaf   _____

moose   _____

Listen to your teacher say each word. Write the words on the lines.

1. _____

2. _____

3. _____

4. _____

5. _____

6. _____

Overview   Prefixes un- and dis-

Directions and Sample Answers for Activity Pages

Day 1	See "Model the Skill" below.
Day 2	Read the title and directions aloud. Invite students to look up each word in the dictionary and decide if the prefix means "not" or "the opposite of." Have students complete the chart with a partner. Have them choose one **un-** word and one **dis-** word and use them in sentences. (not: **unable, dislike, distrust**; the opposite of: **unbend, uncap, discolor**)
Day 3	Read the title and directions aloud. Invite students to look at the words and then add **un-** or **dis-** to each word. Have students write the new word on the line. Have students read each word to a partner. Have students choose three words and draw illustrations of what the words mean. (**un: unaware, unpaid, unfinished, unmade; dis: discharge, disorder, disgrace, displace**)
Day 4	Read the title and directions aloud. Invite students to read each word and each sentence. Have students fill in the blanks with the correct word. (**display, unhappy, unafraid, uncover, disappeared, unplug, dishonest, disappointed, unhealthy**)
Day 5	Read the directions aloud. Allow time for students to complete the first task. (**unclean, disorder, disarray, unfair, disallow, unwind**) Next, pronounce the words **unable, unpack, dislike,** and **discolor** and ask students to write them on the lines. Afterward, meet individually with students. Ask them to read each word on the assessment page. Discuss their results. Use their responses to plan further instruction and review.

Model the Skill

◆ Hand out the Day 1 activity page. Then write the word **unkind** on the board. **Say:** *A prefix is a group of letters at the beginning of a word that changes the meaning of the word. The prefix* **un** *means "not" or "the opposite of." Look at* **unkind**. *The base word is* **kind**. *Adding* **un-** *to* **kind** *changes the meaning of the word from "kind" to "not kind."* Write the following sentence under **unkind**: *You were unkind when you took my pencil.*

◆ Write the word **unpack** on the board. **Say:** *Now look at* **unpack**. *The base word is* **pack**. *Adding* **un-** *to* **pack** *changes the meaning. In this word, the prefix* **un** *means "the opposite of." The opposite of* **pack** *is* **unpack**. Write the following sentences under **unpack**: *I will pack my clothes before I leave. I will unpack my clothes after I get to the hotel.* **Say:** *Copy what I did.*

◆ Write the words **disobey** and **disappear** on the board. **Say:** *The prefix* **dis** *means the same thing as* **un**. *Look at* **disobey**. *What is the base word for* **disobey**? (**obey**) *Adding* **dis-** *to* **obey** *changes the meaning from "obey" to "not obey."* Repeat with **disappear**: *The magician will disappear from the booth.*

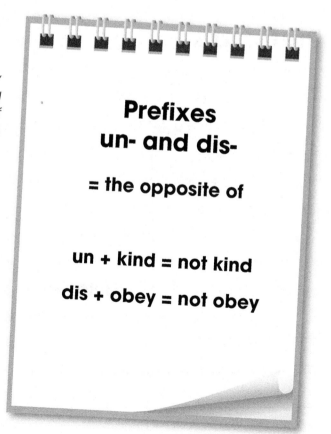

**Prefixes
un- and dis-**

= the opposite of

un + kind = not kind

dis + obey = not obey

Prefix un-

Circle the base word in each example. Then use each word in a sentence.

unkind

unpack

_____
_____
_____

_____
_____
_____

Prefix *dis-*

disobey

disappear

_____
_____
_____

_____
_____
_____

Not or Opposite

Look up the following *un-* and *dis-* prefix words in the dictionary and decide
if the prefix means "not" or "the opposite of." Complete the chart with a partner.

Word	not	the opposite of
unbend		
unable		
uncap		
discolor		
dislike		
distrust		

Choose one *un-* word and one *dis-* word to use in sentences.

1. _____

_____

2. _____

_____

Un or Dis?

Look at the following words. Add *un-* or *dis-* to each word. Write the
new prefix word on the line provided. Read each word to a partner.

aware _____   grace _____

charge _____   finished _____

order _____   made _____

paid _____   place _____

Choose three words and draw illustrations of what those words mean.

Un- or Dis-

**Read the words in the box. Then read the sentences.
Fill in the blanks with the appropriate word.**

unafraid	unhealthy	display
unplug	unhappy	disappeared
uncover	dishonest	disappointed

Tim had his paintings on _____.

Emma was very _____ when her ice cream cone melted.

Cory was _____ when she saw the big dog.

If you take the lid off a pot, you _____ it.

The children _____ when it was time to do their chores.

_____ your phone if you don't want anyone to call you.

Cheating on a test is _____. Your parents would be
very _____.

If you don't eat your vegetables, you will be _____.

Assessment

Read the following words. Add *un-* **or** *dis-* **and write the new word on the line provided.**

clean　　_____

order　　_____

array　　_____

fair　　_____

allow　　_____

wind　　_____

Listen to your teacher say each word. Write the words on the lines.

1. _____

2. _____

3. _____

4. _____

Overview Prefix re-

Directions and Sample Answers for Activity Pages

Day 1	See "Model the Skill" below.
Day 2	Read the title and directions aloud. Invite students to read each base word and prefix word. Then have students illustrate both words showing how the meaning of the base word changes when the prefix **re-** is added. Have students share illustrations with a partner.
Day 3	Read the title and directions aloud. Invite students to read the story and locate the seven **re-** words. Have students write the words on the lines provided and read each word to a partner. (**reconstruct, rebuild, reroof, repays, replace, rechecked, remind**)
Day 4	Read the title and directions aloud. Invite students to read the words in the box and match them to the correct definition. Then locate each **re-** word in the word search. (**reuse, refreeze, reopen, reattach, remix, refill, recut, retag, retie**)
Day 5	Read the directions aloud. Allow time for students to complete the first task. (**repave, regroup, rewash, recount, recall, retrace**) Next, pronounce the words **rewrap**, **repay, remind**, and **reopen** and ask students to write them on the lines. Afterward, meet individually with students. Ask them to read each word on the assessment page. Discuss their results. Use their responses to plan further instruction and review.

Model the Skill

◆ Hand out the Day 1 activity page. Write the following sentence on the board: *I want you to reread the book at home.*

◆ **Say:** *A prefix is a group of letters at the beginning of a word that changes the meaning of the word. The prefix **re-** means "to do again." Listen to this sentence: I want you to reread the book at home.* Circle **re-** in **reread**. *When you reread something, you read it again. **Rereading** also suggests that the text has already been read at least once. Copy what I did.*

◆ Write the words **arrange** and **rearrange** on the board. **Say:** *Look at **rearrange**. When you arrange things, you put them in a certain place. When you rearrange things, you put them in a different place.*

◆ Help students write a sentence using the word **rearrange**. Repeat with **heat** and **reheat** and with **write** and **rewrite**.

Prefix
re-

= again

re + read = read again
re + heat = heat again

Prefix re-

Listen. Then write sentences for each row of pictures.

I want you to reread the book at home.

arrange   **rearrange**

_____

_____

_____

Name _____

Draw Again

Read each base word and prefix word. Draw illustrations that show how the meaning of each base word changes when the prefix *re-* is added. Share the illustrations with a partner.

Base Word		Prefix Word	
wrap		rewrap	
pack		repack	
draw		redraw	
tie		retie	

A Lesson Worth Relearning

Read the title and story and circle the seven _re-_ prefix words.
Write the words on the lines provided. Read each word to a partner.

After the wolf huffed and puffed, he left. Two little pigs looked at their house of sticks, which had tumbled down.

"We'll have to reconstruct our house," the first pig said. "We'll need to rebuild the walls and then reroof it."

"This is how he repays us for dinner?" his brother questioned. "Why should we replace our walls and roof? The next time he comes for dinner, the same thing will happen."

"And I made the soup so carefully. I kept adding pepper, and I checked and rechecked it," whined the first pig.

"Pepper!" exclaimed his brother. "How many times do I have to remind you? Pepper makes the wolf sneeze."

1. _____

2. _____

3. _____

4. _____

5. _____

6. _____

7. _____

Word Search

Read the words in the box. Fill in the blanks with the correct word and then circle the words in the word search.

reattach	**retag**	**refreeze**
reopen	**refill**	**reuse**
recut	**retie**	**remix**

to use again: _____   to fill again: _____

to freeze again: _____   to cut again: _____

to open again: _____   to tag again: _____

to attach again: _____   to tie again: _____

to mix again: _____

r	w	a	r	e	t	i	e	m	r
a	p	r	e	f	r	e	e	z	e
r	e	h	u	r	e	c	u	t	o
e	u	r	s	n	f	r	s	e	p
t	q	r	e	m	i	x	g	t	e
a	r	e	o	i	l	l	u	t	n
g	e	m	o	x	l	a	c	h	n
r	e	a	t	t	a	c	h	x	m

Name _____

Assessment

Read the following words. Add the prefix *re-* to each base word and write the new word on the line provided.

pave   _____

group   _____

wash   _____

count   _____

call   _____

trace   _____

Listen to your teacher say each word. Write the words on the lines.

1. _____

2. _____

3. _____

4. _____